Aromaticity

張　彬　如
BING–RU CHANG

清華化學
1981
張彬如

Consulting Editor

P. Sykes, MSc, PhD

Fellow of Christ's College
University of Cambridge

Aromaticity

P. J. Garratt
Lecturer in Chemistry
University College, London

清華化學
1981 張彬如

Contents

第一章

Preface

For over 150 years chemists have been intrigued and research has been stimulated by that group of unsaturated organic molecules which are ' aromatic '. To the chemist this term implies that a certain set of properties will be found in these molecules, but the basic concept of aromaticity is one which it has not been possible to define. This area has seen a most fruitful interaction between theoretical concepts and experimental observations, and considerable advances in both of these aspects have been made in the last two decades. In this book I have tried to provide both an outline of the problems involved in the concept of aromaticity and a discussion of the groups of molecules to which this concept has been applied. For this purpose the properties of benzene and cyclooctatetraene have been discussed in some detail in the early chapters, and the difference in properties of these two molecules has then been used to provide a framework for the subsequent discussion. The more recent extensions of the aromaticity concept to homoaromaticity, bicycloaromaticity, and aromatic transition studies are considered in the concluding chapters. The book, like its companions in this series, is aimed at the final year honours and the starting postgraduate student. Some general references have been given at the end of each chapter which should enable the reader to follow up any area that he finds of interest. No attempt has been made to cover the field exhaustively, as this would be impossible in a book of this size and scope, and I apologize in advance to any author who considers he has been neglected.

A number of people have read the manuscript, in whole or part, during the course of its preparation. I would like to thank my colleagues, Mr Peter Vollhardt and Dr Reg Mitchell, who read and commented on the complete manuscript; Mr Andrew Holmes, who read the later chapters; Dr T. Thirunamachandran for his gentle criticism and kind advice on the theoretical material in the first two chapters; and Dr Jim Parkin for his comments on the spectroscopic material in these chapters. I would also like to thank Mr J. Creswell for drawing some of the figures, and Miss Angela Rosbaud for converting my execrable handwriting into typescript.

Finally there are two people who must bear a heavy responsibility for the appearance of this book, my friends and mentors Professor Thomas Katz, who initiated my interest into this subject, and Professor Franz Sondheimer who has helped to sustain it.

Acknowledgements. I thank Messrs Butterworths for permission to publish Figs. 2.13 and 8.5; Professor R. McWeeny and Messrs Taylor and Francis Ltd. for permission to publish Fig. 2.11; and Professor J. P. Snyder and Academic Press for permission to publish Figs. 4.18 and 4.19. Figures 3.3 and 3.6 were kindly supplied by Professor F. Sondheimer, and Fig. 3.10 by Professor J. F. M. Oth.

P. J. GARRATT

1. The aromaticity problem

1.1 Introduction

One of the major achievements of nineteenth-century chemistry was the formulation of an empirical theory of valency. This theory resulted largely from the study of organic compounds, the systematic investigation of which was begun in the early part of the century by Wohler and Liebig. Whereas the ionic theory of Berzelius explained much of the inorganic chemistry which was known at the time, Dumas and others clearly demonstrated that this theory was not successful in accounting for the behaviour of organic compounds. Thus, although chlorine and hydrogen were of an opposite nature in the system of Berzelius, chlorine could replace hydrogen in organic systems. Furthermore, as was pointed out by Laurent, in most cases such a *substitution* did not greatly affect the properties of the compound. A second important observation was that groups of atoms in organic molecules appeared to pass unchanged through complex series of reactions. These groups of atoms, such as CH_3 and CH_3CH_2, were called *radicals*. After a long and acrimonious argument between the proponents of the substitution theory and those of the radical theory, these theories were combined by Gerhardt, using the experimental results of Hofmann and of Williamson, into his ' Theory of Types '. In this theory the hydrogen atoms of the parent system of the type were successively replaced by organic ' radicals '. Thus methanol, CH_3OH, was of the water type, one of the hydrogens in H_2O having been replaced by the CH_3 radical. Dimethyl ether, CH_3OCH_3, was also of the water type, but in this case both of the hydrogens have been replaced by CH_3 radicals.

A second problem, which was resolved at about the same time, was the question whether atomic or equivalent weights should be used in the formulation of organic molecules. Berzelius had established excellent values for the atomic weights of many of the elements earlier in the century, but unfortunately his atomic weight for carbon was the most seriously in error. Because of this, some chemists had come to favour the use of equivalent weights, with carbon having a value of 6, for the composition of organic compounds. Complete confusion resulted, since, for example, H_2O_2 could be the formula of either water or hydrogen peroxide! However, at the Karlsruhe Conference in 1860, Cannizzaro circulated a pamphlet which, although it did not lead to immediate agreement on a single system, had a profound effect on the Conference participants. In this pamphlet the Italian chemist summarized his previously reported results and explained how, by the use of Avogadro's hypothesis, a unique system of atomic weights could be obtained applicable to both organic and inorganic compounds. Most chemists accepted these findings, and molecular formulae could now be established on which all would agree.

Just before the Karlsruhe Conference, in 1857, Kekulé had recognized that, using the new atomic weights of Cannizzaro, carbon appeared to be tetravalent in a number of compounds. In his celebrated paper of 1858 Kekulé extended this view to all carbon compounds, and introduced the further concept that carbon atoms could be linked to one another. Similar views were put forward independently by Couper, who used a dotted line to represent a valency bond. These ideas were developed for other atoms, and it was concluded that each atom has one or more possible valencies. The belief that the formula now represented an arrangement of atoms began to be more commonly accepted, and structural formulae were introduced by Crum Brown. These structural formulae were then shown to require modification to express the three-dimensional nature of the molecules, and the concept of the tetrahedral arrangement of the carbon valencies was independently advanced by van't Hoff and Le Bel.

A number of carbon compounds, such as carbon monoxide, did not conform to the Kekulé–Couper theory of tetravalent carbon. The unsaturated hydrocarbons ethylene, C_2H_4, and acetylene, C_2H_2, were two further exceptions to the rule, and three serious explanations were put forward to account for the apparent lack of tetravalency of carbon in these systems. Couper proposed that carbon could be divalent as well as tetravalent; Kekulé suggested that some of the carbon valencies were unsatisfied; and Erlenmeyer proposed that the carbons were linked to each other with more than one valency. Benzene and the aromatic compounds raised further complications, since these molecules, unlike ethylene and acetylene, do not readily undergo addition reactions to give derivatives in which carbon is tetravalent. The paradox of benzene, unsaturated and yet inert, is the central theme of this book. The ramifications of this problem will lead us far away from benzene, but it remains the aromatic compound *par excellence*, and will be the subject of discussion in the rest of this chapter and much of the next.

1.2   Early investigations into the structure of benzene

Benzene was discovered by Faraday in 1825 in the condensate obtained by compression of the gas generated by pyrolysis of whale oil. Faraday determined the composition, CH, the vapour pressure, and the melting point

(42°F). The first synthesis of benzene was accomplished by Mitscherlich in 1833 by the decarboxylation of benzoic acid. Mitscherlich assigned the correct molecular formula, C_6H_6, to benzene on the basis of the vapour density, and subsequently synthesized a number of derivatives.

Benzene was recognized as the parent of a number of compounds which all contained the C_6H_5 radical, and this radical was shown to be inert, remaining intact throughout series of chemical reactions. Benzene did not fit into the Kekulé–Couper tetravalent theory of carbon, and joined the unsaturated hydrocarbons ethylene (C_2H_4) and acetylene (C_2H_2) in providing difficulties for this theory.

The first satisfactory formula for benzene was put forward by Kekulé in 1865. In this formulation, the six carbon atoms of benzene were considered to be linked alternatively by one and two valencies, which left eight valencies unsatisfied. Two of these unsatisfied valencies were then used by linking the terminal carbon atoms to form a *cyclic system*. The six carbon atoms then had six unused valencies to which the six monovalent hydrogen atoms could be attached. This was originally illustrated by Kekulé in the structure shown in Fig. 1.1 (i), in which the ellipses represent the carbon atoms, the lines the bonds between the carbon atoms, the dots the points of attachment of the hydrogen atoms, and the arrows indicate the junction of the terminal carbon atoms. Subsequently Kekulé modified these concepts, and introduced the now familiar hexagon structure with alternate double and single bonds (Fig. 1.1 (ii)).

(i)   (ii)

Figure 1.1 Structures for benzene suggested by Kekulé. For a description of structure (i) see the text.

The hexagonal formula predicts that all six carbon atoms, but not the six bonds, in benzene are equivalent, and this prediction was confirmed by investigations carried out independently by Ladenburg and Wroblewsky. Wroblewsky prepared the five possible *mono*-bromobenzoic acids, using suitable blocking groups which could be subsequently removed, and he found that the 1,2 and 1,6 and also the 1,3 and 1,5 derivatives were identical (Fig. 1.2). Thus carbons 2 and 6, and 3 and 5 are identical. Ladenburg had previously found that the three isomeric hydroxybenzoic acids gave the same phenol on decarboxylation, and the same benzoic acid on reduction. The phenol was then converted to benzoic acid, which was shown to be

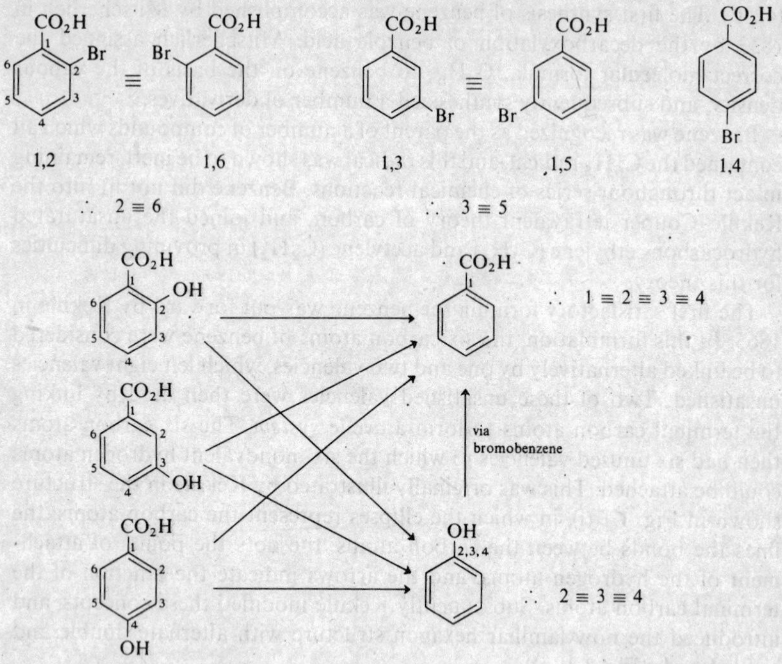

CO_2H Br $\equiv$ Br CO_2H

1,2   1,6

∴ 2 ≡ 6

CO_2H Br $\equiv$ CO_2H Br

1,3   1,5

∴ 3 ≡ 5

CO_2H Br

1,4

CO_2H OH (positions 6,5,4,3,2)

CO_2H OH (1,3,5 positions)

CO_2H OH (1,4 positions)

CO_2H

∴ 1 ≡ 2 ≡ 3 ≡ 4

via bromobenzene

OH _{2,3,4}

∴ 2 ≡ 3 ≡ 4

Figure 1.2

identical with the benzoic acid obtained by reduction. Thus the carbon atoms at positions 1, 2, 3, and 4 are equivalent. The combination of this data with Wroblewsky's demonstrates that the six carbon atoms are equivalent to each other (Fig. 1.2).

These experiments now placed the requirement on any suggested structural formula for benzene that all the carbon atoms must be equivalent.

Ladenburg now protested that Kekulé's hexagon formula required *four*, rather than the *three* disubstituted products which had been prepared (Fig. 1.3). To counter this objection, Kekulé introduced the concept that

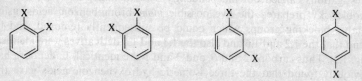

Figure 1.3 The four possible disubstituted benzenes assuming the static Kekulé hexagonal structure.

there were two equivalent hexagon structures for benzene, **1a** and **1b** (Fig. 1.4) which rapidly interconverted by a 'mechanical motion'. This 'mechanical motion' is equivalent to the oscillation of the double bonds around the ring, and the interchange between **1a** and **1b** renders the two 1,2-disubstituted derivatives in Fig. 1.3 equivalent.

Although the 'resonating' structures for benzene appear to us as an example of Kekulé's intuitive genius, at the time it was introduced the idea

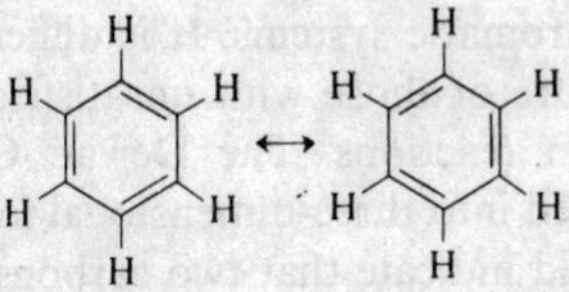

1a   **1b**

Figure 1.4

was considered to be a mere device to save the hexagon theory. Many other structures for benzene were proposed, such as the 'para' bonded formula **2** by Dewar and Wislicenus, and the 'diagonal' formulae **3** and **4** by Claus. We now recognize that such formulae have stereochemical implications as three-dimensional structures, but this was not completely recognized at the time. Ladenburg, however, also proposed formula **4** for benzene, and subsequently recognized the three-dimensional properties of 'Ladenburg's Prism' (**5**). Ladenburg believed that the prism formula was consistent with

2   **3**   **4**   ≡   **5**

the observation that only one disubstituted benzene was known, but van't Hoff demonstrated that the prism formula requires that enantiomeric 'ortho' forms should exist.

Kekulé's formulation continued to provide conceptional difficulties to many workers. Lothar Meyer and Armstrong independently proposed a model in which the six unused valencies were directed towards the centre of the hexagon (**6**), and this formulation was adopted by Baeyer (**7**). Bamberger extended this type of formulae to naphthalene (**8**) and to heterocyclic systems, such as pyrrole (**9**). Bamberger recognized that in these systems *six* unsatisfied valencies are required for each ring, and he clearly considered that this arrangement must provide a stabilized inert system.

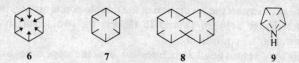

6   **7**   **8**   **9**

These structural theories for benzene are a remarkable achievement of nineteenth-century chemistry, but they do not explain the lack of reactivity of benzene and related aromatic systems. It is difficult to understand why either the Kekulé structure or those with unsatisfied valencies should not readily undergo addition reactions. The Dewar, Claus, and Ladenburg structures, when translated into three-dimensional forms, are unacceptable. Dewar's structure **2** would indicate that two carbons are different from the other four, besides having the stereochemical implications shown in formula **10**. The diagonal formula **3** of Claus is not translatable into three-dimensional terms with reasonable bond angles (Fig. 1.5).

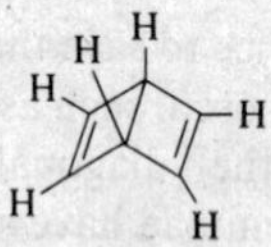

10

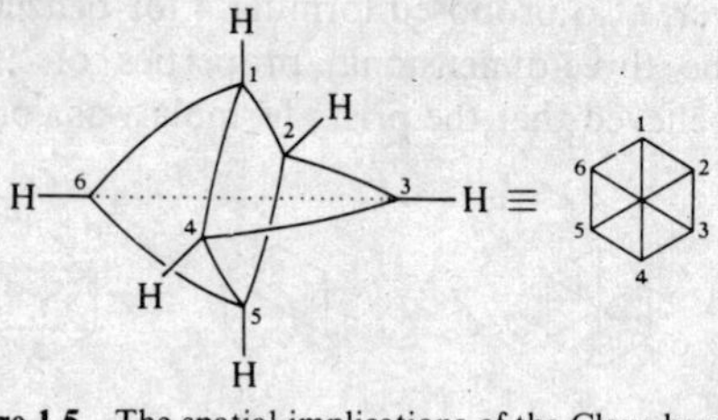

Figure 1.5   The spatial implications of the Claus benzene formula.

Bamberger had realized the importance of the sextet of affinities in benzene, and had, as we have previously seen, used this concept to explain the aromaticity of other systems. The first major attempt to account for the lack of reactivity of benzene was, however, provided by Thiele within the framework of his theory of partial valency. To account for the 1,4-addition of reagents to butadiene, Thiele suggested that the diene had partial unsatisfied valencies at the terminal atoms, and a partial double bond between the central carbon atoms. When this concept is applied to benzene, the terminal unsatisfied affinities are now shared by the 1,6 carbon atoms, and a structure is obtained in which all of the bonds have a character similar to the central bond of butadiene (Fig. 1.6). Thiele's structure of benzene suggests that all cyclic

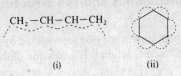

(i)   (ii)

Figure 1.6 The structures of butadiene (i) and benzene (ii) according to Thiele's theory of partial valency.

polyenes should have similar properties to benzene, and the synthesis of cyclooctatetraene (**11**) by Willstäter and his co-workers, which had the properties of an olefin rather than those of benzene, caused Thiele's view to fall out of favour.

11

During the period between Kekulé's formulation for benzene and Willstätter's synthesis of cyclooctatetraene, a revolution in our understanding of the nature of matter had occurred. The electron had been discovered by Thomson, and this had led to attempts to correlate affinity with electron availability. In 1916, Kossel and Lewis gave an interpretation of atomic structure in which the electrons occupied shells, with two electrons in the first shell, and eight electrons in the two subsequent shells. When these shells are filled, the inert gas structure results. Thus, with the inner two-electron shell filled the helium configuration is reached, and with the two-electron and first eight-electron shells filled the ten-electron neon structure is attained. These ideas were significantly extended by Lewis in his suggestion that the atoms forming a molecule can *share* electrons so that each may attain an inert gas configuration. This proposal embodies the concept of the ' localized bond ', formed by the sharing of two electrons.

The electronic theory of valency was applied to benzene by Armit and Robinson and by Ingold. Armit and Robinson supposed the six free affinities to be six electrons, and they re-interpreted Bamberger's theory in terms of the ' *aromatic sextet* ' of electrons which, like the octet, was presumed to have a closed configuration. Ingold extended the Kekulé model to include the three Dewar structures with ' para ' bonds between the 1,4, 2,5, and 3,6 atoms respectively, and formulated benzene as a combination of all five structures.

Neither the Robinson–Armit nor Ingold theories accounts for the stability of benzene. However, during the 'twenties quantum mechanics was invented, and arising from this, theories of chemical bonding were developed by which it is possible to account for the stability of the ' aromatic sextet '. These theories will be discussed in the next section.

7

1.3 Quantum mechanics and the structure of complex molecules

The state of a molecular system may be represented by a function ψ, called the wavefunction. The wavefunction ψ is a solution of the Schrödinger wave equation

$$H\psi = E\psi \tag{1.1}$$

in which H is the Hamiltonian operator which is associated with the observable energy of the system, E. This equation has in general discrete solutions ψ_i called *eigenfunctions*, and the corresponding energies E_i of these eigenfunctions are *eigenvalues*. The solution ψ_0 corresponding to the lowest eigenvalue E_0 represents the ground state of the system, and the other solutions of ψ_i corresponding to higher eigenvalues represent excited states. In general the Schrödinger equation is only analytically soluble for one-electron systems such as the hydrogen atom or the hydrogen molecular ion, $H_2^{\oplus}$. For complex systems approximate methods must be used, and the most useful of these is the *variation method*. The *variation principle* states that the mean value of the energy calculated using the function ψ_i is never less than the energy of the lowest eigenstate E_0. Thus

$$E_0 \leqslant E = \frac{\int \psi_i H \psi_i \, d\tau}{\int \psi_i \psi_i \, d\tau} \tag{1.2}$$

The value of the trial function ψ_i is then varied so that the value of E more closely approaches E_0. The usual method of obtaining the trial functions ψ_i is to take linear combinations of the atomic orbitals (LCAO) of the atoms involved, such that

$$\psi_i = \sum_r c_{ir} \phi_r \tag{1.3}$$

where ϕ_r is the atomic orbital on the rth atom, and c_{ir} is the coefficient of that orbital.

Now if eq. (1.3) is substituted into eq. (1.2), then eq. (1.4) and (1.5) can be obtained.

$$E = \frac{\int \left(\sum_r c_r \phi_r \right) H \left(\sum_r c_r \phi_r \right) d\tau}{\int \left(\sum_r c_r \phi_r \right)^2 d\tau} \tag{1.4}$$

$$= \frac{\sum_r \sum_s c_r c_s \int \phi_r H \phi_s \, d\tau}{\sum_r \sum_s c_r c_s \int \phi_r \phi_s \, d\tau} \tag{1.5}$$

Denoting $\int \phi_r H \phi_s \, d\tau$ by H_{rs}, and $\int \phi_r \phi_s \, d\tau$ by S_{rs}, then eq. (1.5) can be expressed as

$$E = \frac{\sum_r \sum_s c_r c_s H_{rs}}{\sum_r \sum_s c_r c_s S_{rs}} \tag{1.6}$$

The coefficients c_r and c_s can now be independently varied so that E tends towards zero. This is accomplished by setting each of the partial derivatives $\partial E / \partial c_i$ equal to zero, which then provides a set of secular equations

$$c_1(H_{11} - S_{11}E) + c_2(H_{12} - ES_{12}) \cdots c_n(H_{1n} - ES_{1n}) = 0$$
$$c_1(H_{21} - S_{21}E) + c_2(H_{22} - ES_{22}) \cdots c_n(H_{2n} - ES_{2n}) = 0$$
$$\vdots \qquad\qquad \vdots \qquad\qquad \vdots \tag{1.7}$$
$$c_1(H_{n1} - S_{n1}E) + c_2(H_{n2} - ES_{n2}) \cdots c_n(H_{nn} - ES_{nn}) = 0$$

These may be expressed in a more compact form as

$$\sum_r c_r(H_{rs} - ES_{rs}) = 0 \tag{1.8}$$

There is an algebraic theorem which states that a set of simultaneous equations have nontrivial solutions (i.e., not solutions in which $c_1 = c_2 = c_n = 0$) only when the determinant formed from the coefficients c_i vanishes. The secular determinant corresponding to (1.7), which must be equated to zero, is (1.9).

$$\begin{vmatrix} H_{11} - ES_{11} & H_{12} - ES_{12} & \cdots & H_{1n} - ES_{1n} \\ H_{21} - ES_{21} & H_{22} - ES_{22} & \cdots & H_{2n} - ES_{2n} \\ \vdots & \vdots & \vdots & \\ H_{n1} - ES_{n1} & H_{n2} - ES_{n2} & \cdots & H_{nn} - ES_{nn} \end{vmatrix} = 0 \tag{1.9}$$

This equation can be solved to give values for the energy of the system. It is, however, often convenient at this stage to make certain approximations to simplify the problem. The approximations introduced by Hückel are discussed in the next section, with particular reference to benzene.

1.4 The Hückel method and its applications to benzene

The benzene molecule contains 12 nuclei and 42 electrons and it would be an enormous task to calculate the wavefunctions by the method described in the previous section. Indeed, even if such calculations were carried out, the resulting wavefunctions would bear no relation to concepts such as the chemical bond. Major approximations are therefore made which substantially simplify the problem.

The carbon and hydrogen nuclei, together with the carbon $1s^2$ electrons are assumed not to take part in the bonding and are neglected. The problem is thus reduced to the remaining 30 electrons, the valence electrons, of which 4 are contributed by each carbon and 1 by each hydrogen. The configuration of the carbon atoms is assumed to be $sp_xp_yp_z$, and the s, p_x, p_y orbitals are combined together to form three hybrid orbitals arranged at 120° from each other in a plane. Two of these hybrid orbitals are used to bond with two other carbon atoms and the third to bond to the hydrogen atom. The six carbons and six hydrogens thus form a hexagonal structure, and the orbitals concerned in this bonding, which are symmetric with respect to the molecular plane, are called σ orbitals. The hexagonal structure is then formed from σ bonds, and this is shown in Fig. 1.7. The σ framework of benzene has required us to

Figure 1.7   The σ framework of benzene.

use 24 of the 30 valence electrons, and the remaining 6 electrons are in the p_z orbitals. These latter orbitals are antisymmetric with regard to the plane of the hexagon, and are termed π-orbitals. It is the 6 electrons in the π-orbitals which are responsible for the aromatic properties of benzene, and these 6 π-electrons can now be treated separately. The separation of the π-electrons from the σ electrons is known as the *Hückel approximation*.

Hückel now developed a method, the Hückel Molecular Orbital Method (HMO), in which the π-electrons can be treated by eq. (1.9). In the HMO method a number of simplifications are introduced into this equation.

The integral H_{rr}, termed the *coulomb integral*, is considered to have a value which depends only on the characteristic atomic orbital ϕ_r of the atom on which it is centred. The coulomb integral is an approximate measure of the electron attracting power of the atom involved, and it is assumed to be independent of the rest of the system. The coulomb integral for carbon, in the HMO method, is given by

$$H_{rr} = \alpha \qquad (1.10)$$

The integral H_{rs} is called the *resonance integral*, and it is a measure of the binding power of the bond rs. H_{rs} is assumed to become vanishingly small except when r and s are nearest neighbours. The Hückel method assumes

$H_{rs} = 0$ when r and s are *not* joined by a σ bond. For carbon atoms which are nearest neighbours

$$H_{rs} = H_{sr} = \beta \qquad (1.11)$$

The integral S_{rs} is called the *overlap integral* and it has the value 0·25 for nearest neighbours. This value becomes rapidly smaller for non-nearest neighbours, and as a consequence H_{rs} vanishes in these cases (see above). The HMO method assumes that $S_{rs} = 0$ when $r \neq s$, and it is self-evident that $S_{rr} = 1$.

Using these approximations, eq. (1.9) can be applied to the 6 atomic π-orbitals which are shown in Fig. 1.8. The 6 atomic π-orbitals combine

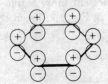

Figure 1.8

to give a six term secular equation which generates six molecular orbitals. Using the integrals defined above, then

$$H_{11} = H_{22} = H_{33} = H_{44} = H_{55} = H_{66} = \alpha$$
$$H_{12} = H_{23} = H_{34} = H_{45} = H_{56} = H_{61} = \beta$$

and

$$H_{13} = H_{14} = H_{15} = H_{24} = \text{etc} = 0$$

The secular equation (1.9) now has the form (1.20)

$$\begin{vmatrix} \alpha - E & \beta & 0 & 0 & 0 & \beta \\ \beta & \alpha - E & \beta & 0 & 0 & 0 \\ 0 & \beta & \alpha - E & \beta & 0 & 0 \\ 0 & 0 & \beta & \alpha - E & \beta & 0 \\ 0 & 0 & 0 & \beta & \alpha - E & \beta \\ \beta & 0 & 0 & 0 & \beta & \alpha - E \end{vmatrix} = 0 \qquad (1.20)$$

The determinant can be simplified by dividing through by β and setting $(\alpha - E)/\beta = x$, which gives (1.21)

$$\begin{vmatrix} x & 1 & 0 & 0 & 0 & 1 \\ 1 & x & 1 & 0 & 0 & 0 \\ 0 & 1 & x & 1 & 0 & 0 \\ 0 & 0 & 1 & x & 1 & 0 \\ 0 & 0 & 0 & 1 & x & 1 \\ 1 & 0 & 0 & 0 & 1 & x \end{vmatrix} = 0 \qquad (1.21)$$

Equation (1.21) can then be solved and the six roots determined. These give six solutions for the energy, $E = \alpha - 2\beta$, $E = \alpha - \beta$ (two roots), $E = \alpha + \beta$ (two roots) and $E = \alpha + 2\beta$. Since β is a negative energy quantity then positive coefficients of β represent more stable energy levels. The energy levels of benzene are shown in Fig. 1.9. From the earlier discussion, since

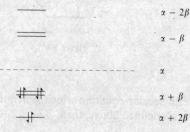

$$\alpha - 2\beta$$
$$\alpha - \beta$$
$$\alpha$$
$$\alpha + \beta$$
$$\alpha + 2\beta$$

Figure 1.9

H_{rr} measures the electron affinity of a carbon atom and is equal to α, then a molecular orbital with an energy α has the same energy as the atomic orbital from which it was derived. Molecular orbitals of energy α are therefore termed *nonbonding molecular orbitals* (NBMO). Orbitals which have energies in which the coefficient of β is positive have lower energies than the $2p$ atomic orbitals from which they were derived and are therefore *bonding orbitals*, whereas those with negative coefficients of β have higher energies than the $2p$ atomic orbitals and are *antibonding orbitals*. Each molecular orbital can accommodate two electrons of opposite spin quantum number, and the six π-electrons of benzene can thus enter three bonding orbitals (Fig. 1.9).

The HMO method applied to benzene thus gives an explanation for its stability, in that all six π-electrons are bonding. The reason for the ' magic ' number six, the aromatic sextet, also becomes apparent, since there are only three bonding molecular orbitals available from the cyclic combination of six atomic orbitals, and thus only six π-electrons can be accommodated.

The total energy for the six π-electrons is $6\alpha + 8\beta$. It would be of considerable interest to know the value of β, but this value is difficult to determine, as will be discussed in chapter 2.

The six π-molecular orbitals of benzene are represented in Fig. 1.10. Of the bonding orbitals, the lowest energy $\alpha + 2\beta$ orbital has no nodes and the

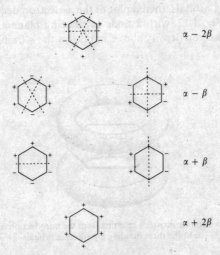

$\alpha - 2\beta$

$\alpha - \beta$

$\alpha + \beta$

$\alpha + 2\beta$

Figure 1.10 The six π-orbitals of benzene, showing the phase of the orbital at each carbon atom and the nodal planes.

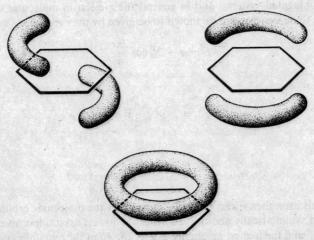

Figure 1.11 A diagramatic representation of the three bonding π-orbitals of benzene. (For clarity only the positive phase of the orbital is shown, the negative phase being the mirror image of the positive phase in the ring plane.)

13

two $\alpha + \beta$ orbitals have one node. In the case of the anti-bonding orbitals, the $\alpha - \beta$ orbitals have two nodes, and the $\alpha - 2\beta$ orbital has three nodes. The phases of the six π-orbitals are indicated in Fig. 1.10. The positive phases of the three bonding orbitals are shown pictorially in Fig. 1.11; the negative phase, which has been omitted for clarity, is the mirror image of the positive phase reflected in the ring plane. When the six π-electrons are introduced into the three bonding orbitals, then a plot of the π-electron density (ψ^2) has the form shown in Fig. 1.12, with a node in the ring plane and two circular regions of high electron density above and below the σ-framework.

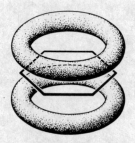

Figure 1.12 The π-electron density (ψ^2) resulting from the introduction of the six π-electrons into the three bonding π-molecular orbitals.

Benzene is a special representative of the group of n-membered monocyclic conjugated systems, and in general the π-electron molecular orbital levels in these systems can be shown to be given by the expression

$$E = \alpha + 2\beta \cos \frac{2\pi r}{n} \qquad (1.22)$$

where

$$r = 0, \pm 1, \pm 2 \cdots \pm \frac{n}{2} \text{ if } n \text{ is even}$$

and

$$r = 0, \pm 1, \pm 2 \cdots \pm \frac{n-1}{2} \text{ if } n \text{ is odd}$$

When n is even then it can be easily shown that the molecular orbitals are arranged symmetrically about α, and that the lowest orbital has an energy of $\alpha + 2\beta$ and the highest an energy of $\alpha - 2\beta$. *All* of the remaining orbitals are *doubly degenerate*. In the case where n is odd, then the lowest orbital is of energy $\alpha + 2\beta$, and the remaining orbitals are *doubly degenerate* (Fig. 1.13).

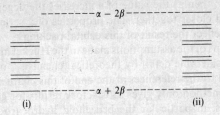

HMO π-orbital pattern for odd (i) and even (ii) monocyclic system.

Since a doubly degenerate orbital can hold 4 electrons, and the lowest molecular orbital can hold 2 electrons, then if the orbitals are filled on the aufbau principle, complete shells of electrons can *only* occur in *mono*cyclic conjugated systems if the system contains $4n + 2$ electrons, where n is an integer. This observation forms the basis of the *Hückel Rule*, which will be discussed further in chapter 2. This finding can be expressed in a simple geometrical form, due to Frost and Musulin. In this method the system is inscribed in a circle of diameter 2β so that one atom is at the bottom of the vertical axis (Fig. 1.14). The horizontal axis now corresponds to the energy

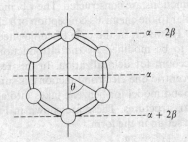

Figure 1.14

level α, and the energies of the orbitals correspond to the positions of the atoms on the circle. Benzene with 6 atoms has n even, and as can be seen in Fig. 1.14, has two nondegenerate orbitals of energy $\alpha + 2\beta$ and $\alpha - 2\beta$. Of the four remaining molecular orbitals, the degenerate bonding orbitals are of energy $\alpha + 2\beta \cos \theta$, where $\theta = 60°$, and thus $E = \alpha + \beta$, while the degenerate antibonding orbitals are of energy $\alpha - 2\beta \cos 60°$, and thus $E = \alpha - \beta$. These values, of course, correspond to those obtained from eq. (1.22). Frost and Musulin diagrams will be used on numerous occasions throughout the rest of this book.

One other consequence of eq. (1.22) should be noted here. Since the lowest molecular orbital is always $\alpha + 2\beta$ and the highest is never more than

$\alpha - 2\beta$ in energy, then as the value of n increases the degenerate levels are forced closer and closer together. The properties of a series of monocyclic systems should reflect the result of this orbital packing.

The implications of the assumptions made in the Hückel method have been discussed in considerable detail by theoretical chemists, and the interested reader is referred to the references at the end of this chapter. It is generally agreed that this method only gives satisfactory results for groups of closely related molecules, in particular the benzenoid hydrocarbons, and that it predicts the order of orbital energies much better than either the total π-energy of the system or the energy difference between orbitals. A further discussion of the shortcomings of the Hückel theory will be found in chapter 2.

1.5 The Valence Bond Method

Besides the molecular orbital method, which has been described in its simplest form above, a second approximate method is available, the valence bond (v.b.) method. Both the m.o. and v.b. methods start by taking atomic orbitals, but whereas in the m.o. model a linear combination of these orbitals is first formed, in the v.b. model wavefunctions similar to Heitler–London two-electron bond functions are constructed. The v.b. model thus gives a picture much more similar to the chemist's conception of a chemical bond than does the m.o. model. However, in the case of conjugated molecules, the simple v.b. model has to be modified by the introduction of a further concept, *resonance*, to account for delocalization. In this respect the m.o. method, which uses polycentric one-electron functions, is superior.

The valence bond model for benzene takes into account the two Kekulé and three Dewar structures. These are shown in Fig. 1.15, and the wavefunctions can be set up in the form

$$\psi = c_1\Theta_1 + c_2\Theta_2 + c_3\Theta_3 + c_4\Theta_4 + c_5\Theta_5 \qquad (1.22)$$

where c_1 is the coefficient and Θ_1 the wavefunction of structure 1. The Kekulé structures are much more important than the Dewar structures, and this will be expressed in the value of the coefficients. Other structures, such as dipolar structures, may also be added, but the coefficients will again be small.

Figure 1.15

The wavefunctions ψ can be evaluated in terms of the coulomb integral Q, which closely corresponds to H_{rr} in the HMO treatment, and the exchange integral J, which represents the interchange of two electrons between *one* pair of carbon atoms. The π-electron energies of benzene can be evaluated in these terms, a 5×5 secular determinant being formed, the roots of which have the value of $E = Q + 2 \cdot 16J$, $Q - 4 \cdot 16J$, Q, $Q - 2J$ and $Q - 2J$. The lowest energy has the value $E = Q + 2 \cdot 16J$, while the energy of a single Kekulé structure is $Q + 1 \cdot 5J$. The difference in energy, $0 \cdot 66J$, represents the increase in stability of benzene over the simple Kekulé structure. Thus the v.b. method, like the m.o. method, accounts for the stability of benzene. The v.b. method can be applied to other aromatic systems, but the application becomes more difficult as the systems become more complex and the number of contributing structures increases.

1.6 Conclusions

By the end of the 'thirties, an explanation for the stability of benzene was thus available in quantum mechanical terms. The conclusions of both m.o. and v.b. methods with regard to benzene are the same, but in the simple form which we have just described the predictions of the m.o. method regarding systems homologous to benzene are different from the predictions of the v.b. method. The nature of these predictions, and how they have been fulfilled, will be the subject of succeeding chapters.

Further reading

For more detailed discussion of the historical aspects of the benzene problem, see J. R. Partington, *A History of Chemistry*, Volume 4, Macmillan, 1964; C. K. Ingold, *Structure and Mechanism in Organic Chemistry*, 2nd Ed., Cornell University Press, 1969; J. P. Snyder in *Nonbenzenoid Aromatics*, Volume 1, ed. J. P. Snyder, Academic Press, 1969.

For general accounts of the m.o. and v.b. theories see C. A. Coulson, *Valence*, 2nd Ed., Oxford University Press, 1962; A. Streitweiser, *Molecular Orbital Theory for Organic Chemists*, Wiley, 1961; T. E. Peacock, *Electronic Properties of Aromatic and Heterocyclic Molecules*, Academic Press, 1965; J. N. Murrell, S. F. A. Kettle, and J. M. Tedder, *Valence Theory*, 2nd Ed., Wiley, 1970; L. Salem, *The Molecular Orbital Theory of Conjugated Systems*, W. A. Benjamin, New York, 1966; M. J. S. Dewar, *The Molecular Orbital Theory of Organic Chemistry*, McGraw-Hill, 1969.

2. Cyclobutadiene, benzene, and cyclooctatetraene

2.1 Application of the HMO theory

In the previous chapter we examined the history of the benzene problem, and presented a simple description of its structure in quantum mechanical terms. The HMO theory satisfactorily accounts for the stability of benzene since the 6 π-electrons enter bonding orbitals and form a closed electronic shell. We will now apply the HMO method to the two nearest homologues of benzene, cyclobutadiene (**1**) and cyclooctatetraene (**2**), using the method of Frost and Musulin, assuming that the systems are planar, with equal bond lengths and bond angles. The diagrams are shown in Fig. 2.1, together with that of benzene.

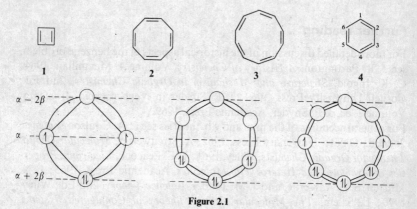

Figure 2.1

A difference in the pattern of orbitals between benzene on the one hand, and cyclobutadiene and cyclooctatetraene on the other, can immediately be observed. Whereas both cyclobutadiene and cyclooctatetraene have two NBMO's of energy α, orbitals of this energy are not present in benzene. Furthermore two of the 4 π-electrons of cyclobutadiene and of the 8 π-electrons of cyclooctatetraene must enter the NBMO's, which are then only partially filled since these orbitals can contain four electrons. The closed shell configuration is thus not duplicated in these models for cyclobutadiene and cyclooctatetraene. Two possible arrangements of the electrons in the NBMO could be made; the electrons could be paired in one orbital with opposite spin, or each could occupy a separate orbital with parallel or anti-parallel spins. Hund's Rule suggests that the latter arrangement with parallel spins will be of lower energy, but the difference in energy between the two states is likely to be small. The state with unpaired electrons will be a triplet diradical, whereas that with paired electrons will be a singlet. Application of the HMO method to planar cyclodecapentaene (3) shows that this system has a closed electronic configuration similar to benzene. Hückel distinguished between these two types of systems; those with $4n$ π-electrons, where n is an integer, have open configurations with electrons in NBMO's, whereas those with $(4n + 2)$ π-electrons have closed electronic configurations. This is the basis for *Hückel's Rule*, which states that planar, monocyclic systems with $(4n + 2)$ π-electrons will be aromatic, whereas those with $4n$ π-electrons will not.

What conclusion does the HMO method come to with regard to the relative stabilities of the localized and delocalized systems? A calculation of a single Kekulé structure for benzene, 4, can be made, taking the same values of the coulombic and resonance integrals, α and β, as were taken for benzene. In this model the π-electron interactions between C2–C3, C4–C5, and C1–C6 are ignored, and the system is treated as a set of three non-interacting ethylenic systems. The determinant is then of the form (2.1), which can be readily reduced to three determinants of the form (2.2).

$$\begin{vmatrix} \alpha - E & \beta & 0 & 0 & 0 & 0 \\ \beta & \alpha - E & 0 & 0 & 0 & 0 \\ 0 & 0 & \alpha - E & \beta & 0 & 0 \\ 0 & 0 & \beta & \alpha - E & 0 & 0 \\ 0 & 0 & 0 & 0 & \alpha - E & \beta \\ 0 & 0 & 0 & 0 & \beta & \alpha - E \end{vmatrix} = 0 \qquad (2.1)$$

$$\begin{vmatrix} \alpha - E & \beta \\ \beta & \alpha - E \end{vmatrix} = 0 \qquad (2.2)$$

The three determinants of type (2.2) give a total of six solutions, three of the form $E = \alpha + \beta$, and three of the form $E = \alpha - \beta$. The six π-electrons can then be put in the three $\alpha + \beta$ orbitals of lower energy, and the total π-energy of 4 is $6\alpha + 6\beta$. The difference in energy between benzene and the Kekulé structure 4 is thus 2β. Similar calculations can be carried out for the planar localized and delocalized forms of cyclobutadiene, cyclooctatetraene, and

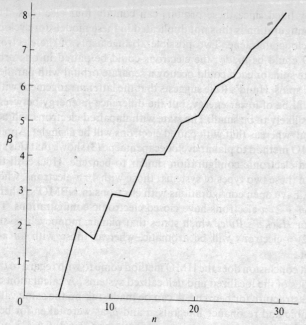

Figure 2.2 The delocalization energy (in β) calculated by the HMO method for monocyclic conjugated systems.

higher homologues of the series. The energy of the localized systems in each case is equal to the product of the number of π-electrons and $(\alpha + \beta)$. The calculated π energies of the localized and delocalized forms of the first four members of the series are shown in Table 2.1, and the results for the series are expressed graphically in Fig. 2.2.

The HMO theory thus predicts that the $(4n + 2)$ π-electron systems will have closed electron shells, whereas those with $4n$ will not, and that there will be a gradual increase in the difference in energy between the localized and delocalized form with increasing ring size. The smaller $(4n + 2)$ π-electron systems are predicted to be more stable than the neighbouring $4n$ π-electron systems, but the difference in stability virtually disappears for the larger rings. The theory specifically predicts that cyclobutadiene will be a square

Table 2.1

System	No of π-electrons	E delocalized	E_0 localized	$E - E_0$
C_4H_4	4	$4\alpha + 4\beta$	$4\alpha + 4\beta$	0
C_6H_6	6	$6\alpha + 8\beta$	$6\alpha + 6\beta$	2β
C_8H_8	8	$8\alpha + 9.66\beta$	$8\alpha + 8\beta$	1.66β
$C_{10}H_{10}$	10	$10\alpha + 12.95\beta$	$10\alpha + 10\beta$	2.95β

planar, triplet diradical with zero resonance energy, that benzene will be a symmetrical hexagon, with considerable resonance energy, and that cyclo-octatetraene will be a planar, octagonal triplet diradical, again with considerable resonance energy.

So far a value has not been assigned to β, and a discussion of its magnitude will be left to later in this chapter. In the next section the experimental evidence for the actual structure of cyclobutadiene, benzene, and cyclo-octatetraene will be discussed, and it will be decided how far these structures conform to those predicted by the HMO theory.

2.2 Experimental evidence for the structures of cyclobutadiene, benzene, and cyclooctatetraene

In the preceding discussion of cyclobutadiene, benzene, and cyclo-octatetraene, the theoretical models used have assumed these systems to be planar, symmetrical systems with all the C—C bonds equivalent. In the present section the experimental evidence for the actual structures will be presented, and compared with the theoretical models. The experimental evidence for the structure of benzene will be described first, as this compound has been the subject of the most extensive investigation.

The resonating Kekulé formulation of benzene predicts that it will be a planar, symmetric hexagon of D_{6h} symmetry, with all of the C—C bonds the same length. The first experimental evidence in support of this structure came not from benzene itself, but from a number of crystalline aromatic compounds (e.g., naphthalene and anthracene) which were investigated by X-ray crystallographic methods by Robertson, Lonsdale, Pinney and others in the late 'twenties and early 'thirties. It was found that the X-ray diffraction data on these compounds were consistent with structures made up of symmetrical hexagons. A particularly relevant study was that of Lonsdale on hexamethylbenzene, in which a planar, hexagonal structure was deduced without any prior assumption that the structure was of this type.

The first conclusive evidence for the D_{6h} symmetry of benzene was adduced by Ingold and his collaborators from an extensive study of the infrared and Raman spectra of benzene and deuterated benzenes. The planar, hexagonal model for benzene requires it to have twenty fundamental vibrations, which can be divided into ten classes in terms of the symmetry of the system. Of these vibrations, seven should be Raman active, four should be infrared active, and the remaining nine should be inactive in either mode. The vibrational spectrum of benzene showed the expected seven fundamental lines in the Raman and four fundamental lines in the infrared spectrum. The Raman spectrum of hexadeuterobenzene, in which the hydrogens are replaced by deuterium, allows the correlation of these bands with the vibrational mode from which they arise. Figure 2.3 shows, diagrammatically, the Raman spectrum of benzene and hexadeuterobenzene. It is readily seen

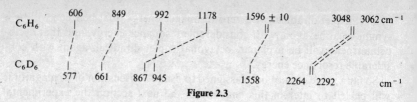

Figure 2.3

that there are two types of lines: Those which are shifted to much longer wavelength in hexadeuterobenzene than in benzene, and those which show much smaller shifts. The bands with the large shifts are those in which the C and H atoms of each C—H unit move *independently* of each other during the vibration, whereas the bands with small shifts are those in which the C—H group moves as a unit in the vibration. In the first case the substitution of deuterium for hydrogen causes a change in the mass ratio of 2:1, whereas in the second case the mass change is 14:13. The band at 3062 cm^{-1} in benzene appears at 2292 cm^{-1} in C_6D_6, and is assigned to the C—H breathing motion, while that at 3048 cm^{-1} is found at 2264 cm^{-1}, and is assigned to a vibrational mode in which the hexagon flattens (Fig. 2.4).

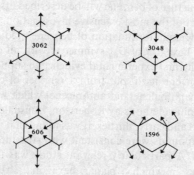

Figure 2.4

In both of these vibrational modes the C—H bond lengths change. The band at 606 cm^{-1} in benzene appears at 577 cm^{-1} in C_6D_6, and is assigned to a vibration in which the hexagon elongates, while the band at 1596 cm^{-1} appears at 1558 cm^{-1}, and is assigned to a vibration in which the atoms at the top and bottom of the hexagon are compressed together (Fig. 2.4). In both of these modes the C—H groups move as units.

The four principal bands in the infrared spectrum of benzene and hexadeuterobenzene are shown diagramatically in Fig. 2.5. A number of other bands were also observed which could be assigned to specific vibrational modes. The forbidden frequencies were identified by examining the spectra of specifically deuterated benzenes, in which the forbidden nature of the vibration is removed by the lower symmetry of the system.

22

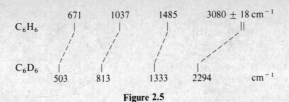

Figure 2.5

Values for the bond lengths in benzene were obtained by Stoicheff from a study of the rotational Raman spectrum of the vapour. The $C{-}C$ bond lengths were 1.397 ± 0.001 Å and the $C{-}H$ bond lengths were 1.084 ± 0.005 Å. An earlier electron diffraction study by Schomaker and Pauling had given values of 1.393 ± 0.02 Å $(C{-}C)$ and 1.08 ± 0.04 Å $(C{-}H)$, and a subsequent X-ray study of crystalline benzene by Cox and his co-workers showed that the molecule was centrosymmetric with $C{-}C$ bond lengths of 1.392 Å. The structure for benzene derived from these and later more refined X-ray data is shown in Fig. 2.6.

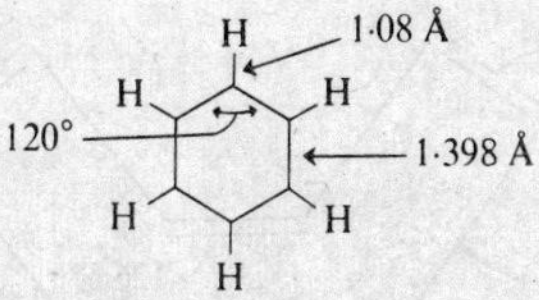

H ← 1·08 Å

120° ← 1·398 Å

Figure 2.6

Cyclooctatetraene is a pale yellow oil which has an ill-defined electronic spectrum which tails into the visible region. A study of the Raman and infrared spectra clearly indicated that cyclooctatetraene is not a planar system of D_{8h} symmetry, since the spectra were too complex with many bands active in both types of spectrum. On the basis of these spectra, Lippincott and his collaborators suggested that cyclooctatetraene could be in either the ' crown ' conformation of D_4 symmetry, or the ' tub ' conformation of D_{2d} symmetry, and they suggested that on balance the data favoured the ' crown ' structure (Fig. 2.7). However, the ' crown ' structure has a considerable disadvantage in that each of the double bonds is strained, the hydrogens not being coplanar, a fact at variance with the thermochemical data (see section 2.3b). Electron diffraction studies, which had originally been interpreted in favour of a planar structure, were repeated with improved resolution, and the new data was interpreted as supporting the ' tub ' structure. The ' tub ' structure was confirmed from an X-ray crystallographic analysis of crystalline cyclooctatetraene, and a combination of electron diffraction and X-ray data gives the structure for cyclooctatetraene shown in Fig. 2.8.

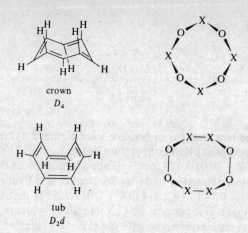

Figure 2.7 'Crown' and 'tub' structures for cyclooctatetraene, showing displacement of the carbon atoms (X, atoms below the plane of the paper; O, atoms above).

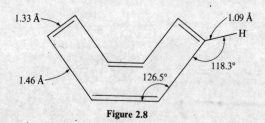

1.33 Å

1.09 Å

H

1.46 Å

126.5°

118.3°

Figure 2.8

Cyclobutadiene is an extremely reactive compound with a short lifetime (see 2.4, p. 37) and no physical data have been obtained. Two possible structures have been considered, the square triplet structure **5** and the rectangular, singlet structure **6**, and the reactions of cyclobutadiene are considered to favour structure **6** (see section 2.4).

5   6

The three compounds which we have discussed are the first three members of the homologous series $(C_2H_2)_n$, and yet they exist in completely different spatial arrangements. Cyclobutadiene is planar, and probably has alternate double and single bonds; benzene is planar, with all C—C bonds equal; and cyclooctatetraene is non-planar, with alternate double and single bonds. That these compounds should differ in properties is predicted by the Hückel Rule, but the stabilization of the planar delocalized form of cyclooctatetraene predicted by the HMO method is not observed.

2.3 Physical properties of benzene and cyclooctatetraene

In this section the physical properties of benzene and cyclooctatetraene which have not been discussed in connection with the structure of these molecules will be considered. Such a distinction is artificial, since much of the data given in this section could, and in fact was, presented as evidence for the structures of these compounds. However, it will now be possible for us to compare the properties of benzene and cyclooctatetraene knowing the difference in structure and shape of these molecules.

(a) *Diamagnetic Anisotropy*. The majority of organic molecules do not have permanent magnetic moments, and consequently are weakly *diamagnetic*, having negative magnetic susceptibilities. This diamagnetism is caused by Larmor precession of the electrons, which produces small magnetic fields opposing the applied magnetic field. The magnitude of this effect depends on the area of the orbit traversed by the electron. Most diamagnetic molecules are anisotropic, that is the magnitudes of the diamagnetic susceptibility along the three mutually perpendicular principal magnetic axes are not equal. In the bulk measurement of the diamagnetism of a compound, the average magnetic susceptibility is measured, but in a single crystal it is possible to determine the magnetic susceptibility along the crystal axes.

Single crystals of a number of benzenoid hydrocarbons, such as naphthalene, show large diamagnetic anisotropies. Krishnan and his collaborators were able to demonstrate that the relationship between the magnetic and crystal axes in these compounds depended upon the orientation of the molecules in the crystal. Furthermore, they found that the magnitude of the magnetic susceptibility along these magnetic axes depended upon the magnetic susceptibilities of the principal axes of the molecule. It was observed that for these benzenoid hydrocarbons, the magnetic susceptibility in the axis at right angles (K^3) to the plane of the ring was greater than that along the axes in the plane of the ring (K^1, K^2) which were approximately equal (Fig. 2.9). For the series of compounds benzene, naphthalene, and anthracene

Figure 2.9

the susceptibilities in the plane of the ring showed only a small increase, whereas that along the normal to the ring plane increased additively with the increase in number of rings (Table 2.2). A similar sequence of values was found for the series biphenyl, tetraphenyl, and quaterphenyl.

Raman and Krishnan, following an earlier theory of Ehrenfest, suggested that the large diamagnetic anisotropy of these systems was due to Larmor

Table 2.2

Compound	$-K^1 \times 10^6$ esu	$-K^2 \times 10^6$ esu	$-K^3 \times 10^6$ esu	$\Delta K \times 10^6$ esu
(benzene ring)	37·3	37·3	91·2	53·9
(naphthalene rings)	39·4	43·0	187·2	146·0
(anthracene rings)	45·9	52·7	272·5	223·2

precession of electrons in orbitals that included many nuclei. This theory was put into a quantitative form by Pauling, and was subsequently interpreted in quantum mechanical terms by London. Pauling showed that the contribution of the electron in a cylindrically symmetric field about the z-axis to the magnetic susceptibility was given by eq. (2.3):

$$\chi = -\left(\frac{Ne^2}{4mc^2}\right)(\rho^2)_{av} \qquad (2.3)$$

In this equation χ is the magnetic susceptibility and $(\rho^2)_{av}$ is the mean square of the distance of the electron from the z-axis. In the Hückel model for benzene only the six π-electrons need be considered. If R^2 is taken to be the value for $(\rho^2)_{av}$, where R is the distance (1·39 Å) from the ring centre to the carbon nuclei of benzene, then the calculated value for the anisotropy, ΔK, was 49,[†] in reasonable agreement with that observed (54, Table 2.2).

This model for benzene, in which the π-electrons precess in molecular orbitals extending over the ring, has subsequently been used to explain the deshielding of aromatic protons in the nmr spectrum. In this model the applied field, H^0, causes the π-electron to circulate in orbitals extending over the six carbon atoms, and a magnetic field H^i, is induced which opposes the applied field. The lines of force resulting from the induced field are shown in Fig. 2.10, and the effect of this induced field is that the apparent field inside

† These, and all subsequent values of magnetic susceptibility, will be in units of 10^{-6} esu.

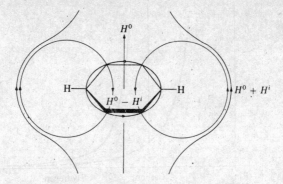

Figure 2.10

the ring is decreased, while the apparent field outside the ring is increased. Protons *outside* the ring therefore resonate at *lower* field than protons uninfluenced by the induced field, whereas protons *inside* the ring will resonate at *higher* field. The use of this model to account for the position of aromatic protons in the nmr spectrum was originally developed by Pople, who, for the purposes of calculation, substituted a point dipole at the centre of the ring for the induced ring current. Waugh and Fessenden improved this model by using a field in which the π-electrons were assumed to be in two identical shells above and below the ring plane. McWeeny developed a quantum mechanical model, in which the induced moment arising from the external field was determined by the method of London. A *point dipole*, m, was then introduced as a probe at the position of the proton in question, and the coupling energy between the point dipole and the induced current distribution was evaluated. The total magnetic energy differs from that with the dipole absent by the coupling term $-mH'$. For benzene the resulting equation gave terms proportional to $1/r^3$ and higher powers, where r is the distance, in bond lengths, of the point dipole from the centre of the ring. At large distances from this ring the expression reduces to the Pople approximation, but in the vicinity of the ring these terms introduce a large correction, increasing the estimated field by up to 80 per cent. Both the McWeeny and Waugh–Fessenden calculations predict that the induced current will be of opposite sign inside and outside the ring, whereas the Pople method predicts that the field increases as the centre is approached. Figure 2.11 compares the McWeeny and Pople models.

Cyclooctatetraene, unlike benzene, does not exhibit enhanced diamagnetic anisotropy, and the value of the magnetic susceptibility is close to that expected for four double and four single bonds. Pink and Ubbelohde found that the calculated magnetic susceptibility for the structure with alternate single and double bonds was -50, and that for the delocalized structure was

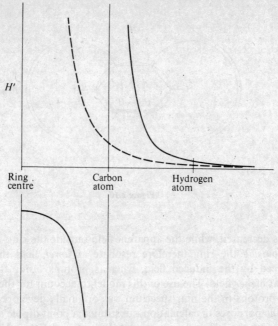

Figure 2.11

−73, while the observed value was −52. These authors also found that the difference in magnetic susceptibility between cyclooctane and cyclooctatetraene was 39·5, close to the predicted value of 41, and in contrast to the difference between cyclohexane and benzene which is 12 instead of the expected 31. In the nmr spectrum, cyclooctatetraene shows a single resonance signal at τ4·32, in the olefinic region. The magnetic properties of cyclooctatetraene are thus those expected for an olefinic system, and cyclooctatetraene does not show the anomalous magnetic behaviour observed in benzene and the benzenoid hydrocarbons.

This method of distinguishing between aromatic and non-aromatic systems has recently been further developed by Dauben and his associates. The original Pascal values used by Pink and Ubbelohde were too inaccurate for a general extension of this method, but recently more accurate values have become available. Using these, and defining the diamagnetic susceptibility exaltation Λ by

$$\Lambda = \chi_M - \chi_{M'} \tag{2.4}$$

(where χ_M is the experimentally determined molar susceptibility of the compound and $\chi_{M'}$ is the estimated molar susceptibility for the corresponding theoretical cyclopolyene) then values of Λ for a large number of systems were obtained. The values obtained show that cyclic non-conjugated olefins have $\Lambda = 0$, that is the Pascal constants are additive, while the benzenoid hydrocarbons show large exaltations. Thus benzene has $\Lambda = 13.7$ and naphthalene has $\Lambda = 30.5$. Aromatic compounds are thus expected to show diamagnetic susceptibility exaltation. Cyclooctatetraene, as would be expected from the earlier results, has $\Lambda = -0.9$, a value close to zero. The exaltation of diamagnetic susceptibility thus seems to be a valid criterion for the determination of aromaticity in a compound. The main problems are that such a determination requires a calculated estimate of the expected susceptibility in the absence of exaltation, which is a similar disadvantage to that found in the determination of resonance energy (see 2.3b), and that the measurement requires fairly large amounts of the compound.

(b) Resonance Energy. When benzene is combusted or hydrogenated, the values obtained from the heat of combustion or hydrogenation do not have the additive values expected for three double bonds of the cyclohexene type. Kistiakowsky and his associates determined the heat of hydrogenation of cyclohexene to be $-28.6 \, kcal.mole^{-1}$. The actual heat of hydrogenation of benzene was found to be $-49.8 \, kcal.mole^{-1}$, and benzene thus has $36.0 \, kcal.mole^{-1}$ less energy available than would be expected. The $36 \, kcal.mole^{-1}$ represents a thermochemical stabilization of benzene, and this has been termed the *resonance energy*.

The heats of combustion and hydrogenation of cyclooctatetraene are close to the values expected for a system with four double bonds. Turner and his collaborators found the heat of hydrogenation of cyclooctatetraene to be $-98 \, kcal.mole^{-1}$, while the value calculated from *cis*-cyclooctene $(-23 \, kcal.mole^{-1})$, would be $-92 \, kcal.mole^{-1}$. This would give a negative resonance energy of $6 \, kcal.mole^{-1}$.

Although arguments can be made against both cyclohexene and cyclooctene as suitable models for comparison, these results clearly demonstrate the complete difference in thermochemical behaviour of benzene and cyclooctatetraene. Whether $36 \, kcal.mole^{-1}$ resonance energy of benzene should be mainly attributed to delocalization of the π-electrons or to the change in σ bond properties is difficult to determine. Clearly cyclohexene is a poor model for benzene, since in the hydrogenation of benzene to cyclohexane, six ' aromatic ' bonds are converted to six ' aliphatic ' bonds. The bonds change in length from $1.39 \, \text{Å}$ to $1.54 \, \text{Å}$, each carbon rehybridizing from an aromatic $sp^2\pi$ to an aliphatic sp^3 type, whereas in the hydrogenation of cyclohexene, the change in bond length is from $1.33 \, \text{Å}$ to $1.54 \, \text{Å}$, and the carbon atoms rehybridize from olefinic $sp^2\pi$ to aliphatic sp^3 type.

In our earlier discussion of the HMO theory, we derived the difference in energy between benzene and a single Kekulé structure as 2β. If we equated this to the resonance energy, the β would have a value of $-18 \, kcal.mole^{-1}$. However, the models used for the determination of the resonance energy and for the calculation are not the same. The value to be assigned to β depends to a large extent on the assumptions made, and estimated values have ranged from -30 to -10 kcal.mole^{-1}. Dewar has given the smaller value to β, from a consideration that the resonance energies have been over-estimated, owing to the use of thermochemical data that ignores the difference between the delocalized system and the model compound. The problem that is involved can be seen in Fig. 2.12. The value for the heat of hydrogenation of benzene, reaction a, is known, and an estimate for the hydrogenation of cyclohexatriene, the reverse of reaction b, can be made from the

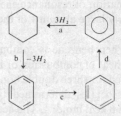

Figure 2.12

heat of hydrogenation of cyclohexene. The delocalization of a single Kekulé structure to benzene is 2β (equation d). The unknown parameter is the energy involved in forming the symmetrical Kekulé structure from cyclohexatriene (equation c), and most thermochemical estimates in fact equate reactions c + d with 2β.

Resonance energy, although it can be readily defined in terms of the extra thermodynamic stability of a molecule over that predicted on the basis of a localized-bond model, is a difficult parameter to determine. The best method for estimating the energy of the localized structure would be by the use of values for the bond energies, which would then be treated additively. In the case of benzene, it would be necessary to know the energies of the 1.39 Å double ' and ' single ' bonds. Unfortunately, such data are not available.

(c) Electronic Spectra. The absorption spectrum of benzene shows three band systems at 255, 205, and 183 nm in the ultraviolet. The long wavelength band at 255 nm is weak and exhibits considerable fine-structure, the 205 nm band is of medium intensity, and the 183 nm band is more intense (Fig. 2.13).

The three transitions may be interpreted as electron jumps from the highest occupied e_{1g} orbital to the lowest unoccupied e_{2u} orbital. There are four possible transitions as shown in Fig. 2.14, and the symmetries of the states obtained from these transitions are formed from the direct product $e_{1g} \times e_{2u} = B_{1u} + B_{2u} + E_{1u}$. A description of these state symbols is given in Table 2.3, and inspection of Fig. 1.10 will confirm that the orbitals of benzene have the characters assigned in Fig. 2.14.

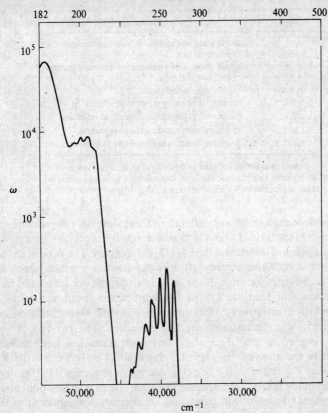

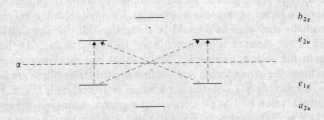

Figure 2.13 Electronic spectrum of benzene in hexane (from H.-H. Perkampus and G. Kassebeer, DMS U.V. Atlas, Butterworths, 1966).

Figure 2.14

Table 2.3

Symbol	Description
a, A	single state, symmetric to rotation around the principal axis
b, B	single state, antisymmetric to rotation around the principal axis
e, E	doubly degenerate state
1	horizontal plane, symmetric to reflection
2	horizontal plane, antisymmetric to reflection
g	inversion centre, symmetric to inversion
u	inversion centre, antisymmetric to inversion

Lower case letters are used to describe orbitals, while upper case letters refer to electronic states. A superscript 1 indicates a singlet state, a superscript 3 a triplet state, e.g. $^1B_{2u}$, $^3B_{2g}$.

In the simple zero-order approximation these states are degenerate, but when electron repulsion is taken into account, this degeneracy is removed, the B_{2u} state being of lowest and the E_{1u} of highest energy. The band at 255 nm was attributed by Sklar to the $^1B_{2u} \leftarrow {}^1A_{1g}$ transition which, since B_{2u} does not transform like an in-plane axis, is electronically forbidden for a $\pi \rightarrow \pi^*$ transition. That the 255 nm band appears in the spectrum is due to a non-totally symmetric e_{2g} vibration mixing in with the excited state and partially removing the restraints on this transition. The band at 205 nm has been assigned to the $^1B_{1u} \leftarrow {}^1A_{1g}$ forbidden transition, and the band at 183 nm to the allowed $^1E_{1u} \leftarrow {}^1A_{1g}$ transition. The latter transition is allowed since E_{1u} transforms like (x, y), and in consequence this transition is polarized in the plane of the benzene molecule. There is some doubt about the assignment of the 205 nm band, and an alternative assignment of this band to an $^1E_{2g} \leftarrow {}^1A_{1g}$ transition has been made. However, on balance the $^1B_{1u} \leftarrow {}^1A_{1g}$ assignment has been more favoured.

A detailed, high resolution rotational analysis of the 255 nm band system of benzene has been made by Callomon, Dunn and Mills, who concluded from this that benzene is *exactly* planar and hexagonal in both the ground and excited states.

If the energies of the ground state and excited state configurations can be determined in terms of the resonance integral β, then from the energies of the transitions the value of β could be determined. In the simple Hückel approach, if one electron is promoted from the highest occupied orbital of benzene to the lowest unoccupied orbital, then the difference in energy between these, the ground state and the first excited states (these are degenerate in this model) is 2β. Assuming a value of 18 kcal.mole^{-1} for β, this would give a value of 1·54 eV between the ground state and the excited states, (1 eV = 23·06 kcal.mole^{-1} = 8055 cm^{-1}), which would give a band at *ca* 800 nm. The Hückel theory grossly underestimates the difference in energy levels between the ground state and excited states. Using more sophisticated methods, with better wavefunctions and including configuration interaction between wavefunctions for a number of electronic states, it is possible to obtain values for the difference in energies more in agreement with those obtained experimentally. van der Lugt and Oosterhoff have recently computed the energy of the various states by a v.b. calculation including all charge separated structures, and compared this with the results of m.o. calculations. The values obtained by these authors, together with experimental values, are shown in Table 2.4.

Table 2.4

Transition	Calculated (eV)	Experimental (eV)
$^1B_{2u} \leftarrow {}^1A_{1g}$	5·22	4·8
$^1B_{1u} \leftarrow {}^1A_{1g}$	6·33	6·0
$^1E_{1u} \leftarrow {}^1A_{1g}$	7·48	7·0

The ultraviolet spectrum of cyclooctatetraene shows no distinct bands, but exhibits a long, diffuse absorption from 220 to 280 nm.

(d) Fluxional Properties. The planar, symmetrical hexagon structure for benzene is the equilibrium configuration of the system, and the vibrational deviations from this structure, which appear in the infrared and Raman spectra, were discussed earlier. The force constants for these vibrations show that benzene can be more easily distorted by out-of-plane vibration than by in-plane vibrations. The bending of benzene rings, as in the paracyclophanes (e.g., 7) is thus not unexpected.

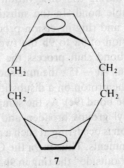

7

Cyclooctatetraene, besides the vibrational changes found in all molecules, also shows fluxional behaviour which occurs at a much slower rate, such that these changes are observed on the nmr time scale (10^{-2} to 10^{-4} s). Two processes have been distinguished, one involving ring inversion and the other the switching of double and single bonds (Fig. 2.15). The process of bond switching was originally observed by Anet from a study in the nmr spectrum of the dependence of the ^{13}C-proton coupling with temperature. The single broad peak due to the ^{13}C coupling which is seen at room temperature splits at lower temperatures to a doublet, due to the different coupling constants across the single and double bonds, which are averaged at room temperature. Thus, in Fig. 2.15, if the molecule contained ^{13}C at C-1, then at

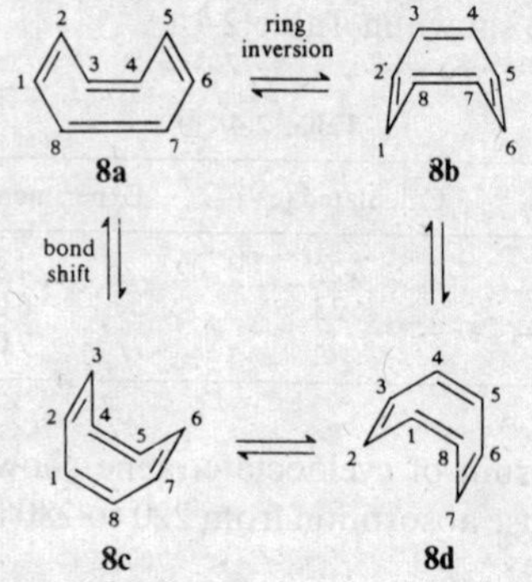

Figure 2.15

room temperature the interconversion of **8a** to **8b** occurs at such a rate that during the observation C-1 is joined to C-2 part of the time by a double bond (**8a**) and part of the time by a single bond (**8b**). On cooling the rate is slowed sufficiently that during the observation C-1 is joined to C-2 by either a single or a double bond. In the substituted cyclooctatetraene **9** both the bond switching and ring inversion processes can be observed. In the course of ring inversion of **9a** to **9b** the two methyl groups are interconverted, while in the bond shift process the positions of the ring substituents change (Fig. 2.16). At $-35°$, the nmr shows discrete methyl signals and discrete signals for the proton on a disubstituted double bond (**9a**) and on a trisubstituted double bond (**9c**). As the sample is allowed to warm the signals due to the methyl groups broaden and coalesce at $-2°$. At this temperature, ring inversion is occurring at such a rate that the methyl groups are interchanging environments. Thus in **9a** the $CH_3{}^b$ which is ' inside ' the ring moves to a position ' outside ' the ring in **9b**. [Free rotation around the C1-C-isopropanol bond does not cause the two methyl groups, which are diastereotopic, to become equivalent.] The rate of bond switching is still sufficiently slow at this temperature for discrete ring protons to be observed, but at $+41°$ the rate has increased so that the signals due to the ring protons in **9a** (**9b**) and **9c** (**9d**) coalesce. The barrier to ring inversion of **9** has an activation energy at $-2°$ of $\Delta G^{\ddagger} = 14.7$ kcal.mole^{-1} while that for bond

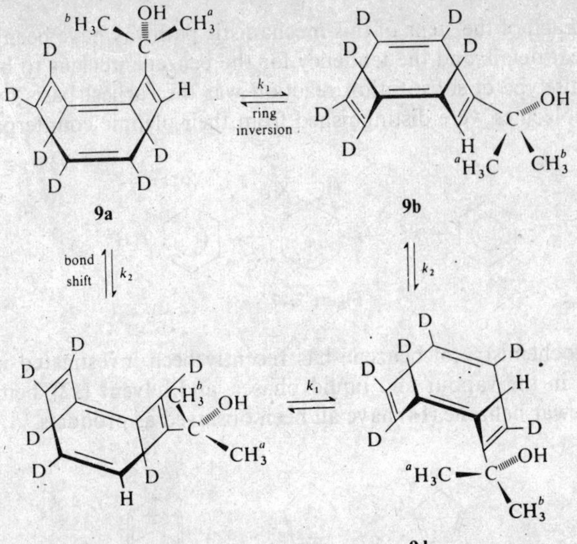

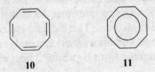

Figure 2.16

switching at the same temperature has $\Delta G^{\ddagger} = 17{\cdot}1$ kcal.mole^{-1}. The transition states for these processes may be considered to be planar; the structure **10** with localized bonds being the transition state for inversion, and **11**, with delocalized bonds, for bond switching. The results suggest that the localized structure **10** is about 2 kcal.mole^{-1} more stable than the delocalized structure **11**. Thus, contrary to the predictions of the HMO theory, the delocalized

10   **11**

structure for planar cyclooctatetraene is *less* stable than the localized bond structure.

2.4 Chemical properties

The chemistry of benzene is extensive, well known, and will not be treated in detail here. The normal mode of attack on the molecule is by electrophilic reagents, and the system passes through a transition state in which the benzenoid character is removed, before expelling a proton to give the product

(Fig. 2.17). Each of the steps of this mechanistic pathway have been investigated in great detail, and the tendency for the benzene nucleus to be maintained in this type of substitution reaction was the earliest basis by which aromatic molecules were distinguished from their olefinic counterparts.

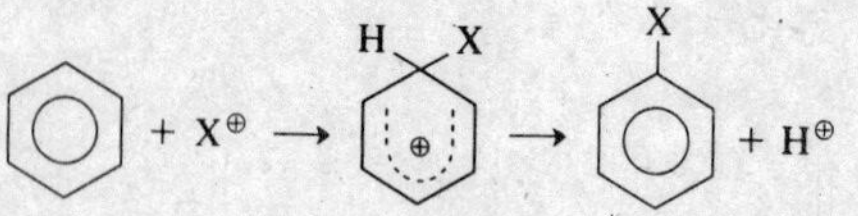

Figure 2.17

The photochemistry of benzene has recently been investigated in some detail, both in the vapour and liquid phases, and fulvene (**12**), benzvalene (**13**), and Dewar benzene (**14**) have all been observed as products.

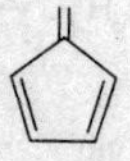

12 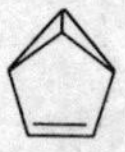   **13**    **14**

Cyclooctatetraene was originally synthesized by Willstätter and his co-workers by successive Hofmann elimination on the alkaloid pseudopelletierine, but is now commercially prepared by the nickel catalysed tetramerization of acetylene. The discovery of this synthetic method by Reppe and his co-workers has led to an extensive chemistry of cyclooctatetraene, which has recently been reviewed by Schröder. The reactions of cyclooctatetraene are largely those expected for an olefin, except that the products often undergo subsequent reactions involving bond reorganization (valence tautomerism). Cyclooctatetraene exists almost exclusively in the monocyclic form **2**, the bicyclic valence tautomer **15** contributing less than 0·05 per cent to the equilibrium mixture. The bicyclic isomer has been prepared at low temperature by Vogel and his co-workers, and it is thermodynamically less stable than the monocyclic form by about 7 kcal.mole^{-1}.

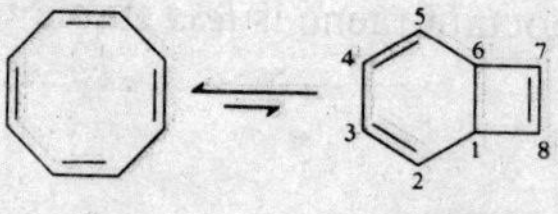

2   **15**

When cyclooctatetraene reacts with halogens, the final products are derived from **15** by addition of halogen across the 7,8 double bond. A study of this reaction has shown, however, that the electrophilic addition occurs to **2** to give the *endo*-chlorohomotropylium cation **16**. The cation **16** then reacts with chloride ions on the *endo* face to give **17**, which valence tautomerizes by a Cope rearrangement to *cis*-7,8-dichlorobicyclo[4.2.0]octadiene (**18**) (Fig. 2.18). The *cis*-stereochemistry of **18** is controlled by the stereoselectivity of attack on **2** and the intermediate **16**. The *exo*-chlorohomotropylium cation gives the *trans* product on subsequent reaction (see chapter 9).

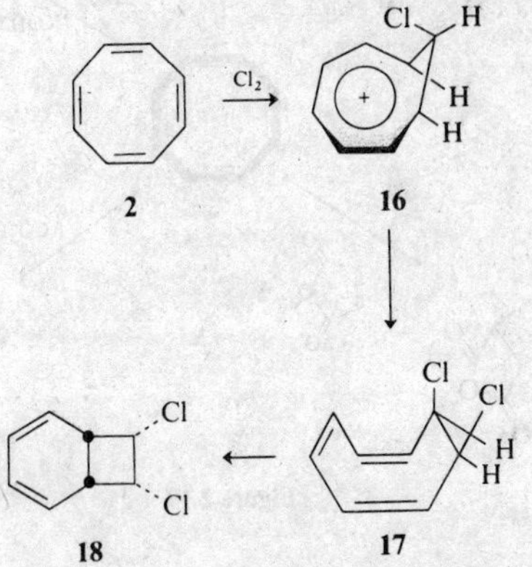

Figure 2.18

Diels–Alder reactions do not occur readily with cyclooctatetraene, and the eventual adducts are derived from **15** (e.g., **19** with maleic anhydride). Epoxidation and carbene addition give products derived from the monocyclic form **2**; and both cyclooctatetraene epoxide (**20**) and the bicyclo[6.1.0] nonatrienes (**21**) are useful synthetic intermediates. Cyclooctatetraene is readily reduced to the dianion **22** with alkali metals, and this reaction is discussed further in chapter 4. Hydration with mercuric sulphate gives phenylacetaldehyde (**23**). These reactions are summarized in Fig. 2.19.

Cyclobutadiene (**1**) is a transient compound, the properties of which have mainly been determined by Pettit and his co-workers from a study of its chemical reactions. Cyclobutadiene is most conveniently generated by oxidation of the iron tricarbonyl complex **24** with ceric ions. The cyclobutadiene which is produced can be trapped with dienophiles to give derivatives of bicyclo[2.2.0]hexadiene (Dewar Benzene) (Fig. 2.20). The bicyclo-[2.2.0]hexadienes (e.g., **25**) readily rearrange thermally to the corresponding substituted benzene (e.g., **26**). In the absence of a dienophile, cyclobutadiene dimerizes by a Diels–Alder reaction to give the tricyclooctadiene **27**, as a mixture of the *syn*- (**27a**) and *anti*- (**27b**) isomers, in the ratio (5:1). Both **27a** and **27b** thermally isomerize to cyclooctatetraene (Fig. 2.21). As previously mentioned, the general chemistry of cyclobutadiene has been interpreted as evidence for the singlet, rectangular ground state, since the

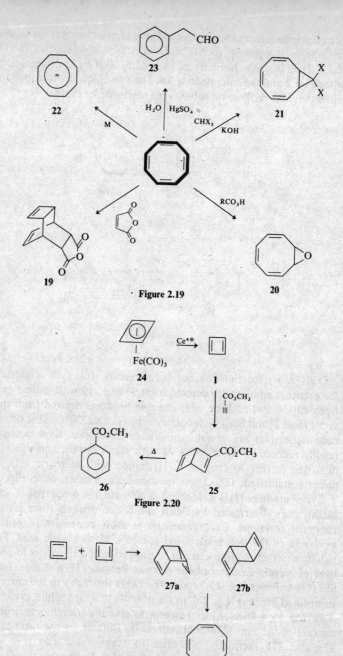

Figure 2.19

Figure 2.20

Figure 2.21

reactions are those of a diene rather than a diradical. The Diels–Alder adducts from dimethyl fumarate and dimethyl maleate are formed stereospecifically and no product that would result from bond rotation is observed (Fig. 2.22). In competition reactions, cyclobutadiene reacts preferentially

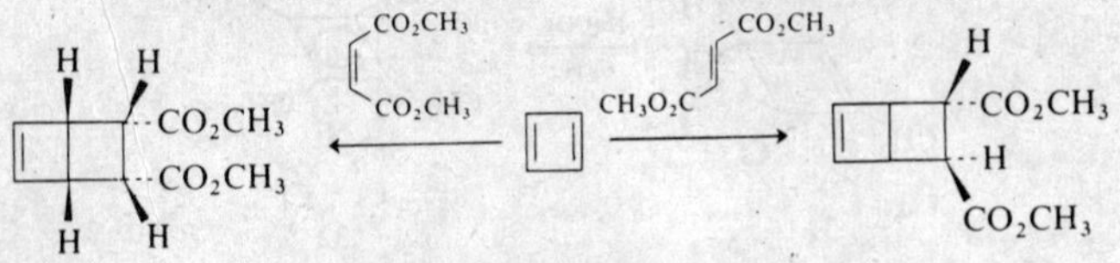

Figure 2.22

with dienophiles rather than with free radical reagents. The reactions of substituted cyclobutadienes suggest that these compounds have rectangular, and not square, cyclobutadiene rings. 1,2-Diphenylcyclobutadiene (28) reacts with tetracyanoethylene to give two adducts, derived from the two possible ortho forms of 28 (Fig. 2.23).

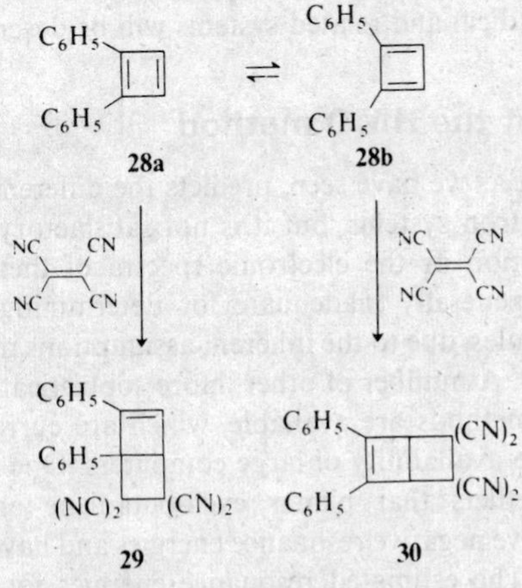

Figure 2.23

Cyclobutadiene is becoming increasingly valuable in synthetic Diels–Alder reactions, as it provides a ready method of forming cyclobutene rings.

The iron tricarbonyl complexes of cyclobutadiene and its derivatives are stable systems. The suggestion that cyclobutadiene would be stabilized by complexing with a suitable transition metal was made by Longuet-Higgins and Orgel, and this prediction was originally verified by Criegee and Schröder, who prepared the nickel chloride complex 32 by treatment of 1,2,3,4-tetramethyl-3,4-dichlorocyclobutene (31) with nickel tetracarbonyl in benzene. The stabilization of **32**, and of the many related systems which have subsequently been prepared, is assumed to arise from the interaction of the molecular orbitals of the ligand with those of the metal. A simple m.o.

calculation indicates that this interaction between the transition metal atom and the ligand produces 8 bonding and 1 nonbonding orbitals. The total electron count should therefore be 16 or 18, depending on whether the NBMO is filled. In **32** the cyclobutadiene supplies 4, the nickel 10, and the chlorine atoms 2 electrons, giving a total of 16 electrons. In the complex **24**, the iron supplies 8 and the carbonyl groups 6, which with the 4 electrons from the cyclobutadiene gives a total of 18 electrons. Filling the NBMO does not therefore appear to be particularly important. Similar complexes of the cyclopentadienyl radical and related systems will be described in chapter 4.

2.5 Validity of the HMO method

The HMO method, as we have seen, predicts the difference between the $4n$ and $(4n + 2)$ π-electron systems, but it is not satisfactory in predicting the resonance stabilization or the electronic spectra of these molecules. The HMO method is generally inadequate for determining the quantitative properties of molecules, due to the inherent assumptions made in the formulation of the theory. A number of other, more sophisticated semi-empirical molecular orbital methods are available, which are currently coming into greater use with the availability of large computers. One of these methods, due to Pople, predicts that planar cyclobutadiene and planar cyclooctatetraene will have negative resonance energies and have alternate double and single bonds. The estimated resonance energies for both the $4n$ and $(4n + 2)$ π-electron systems are less than those predicted by the Hückel method. A comparison of the delocalization energies derived from the Hückel and a Pople–Pariser–Parr calculation is shown in Fig. 2.24.

In the simple HMO theory cyclobutadiene and cyclooctatetraene both have degenerate ground states. The Jahn–Teller theorem postulates that, except for linear systems, molecules with degenerate ground states will be unstable, and that such systems will distort in order to reduce this symmetry. Cyclobutadiene can only distort by a process of bond alternation, and the rectangular state is thus expected to be of lower energy. The magnitude of the Jahn–Teller effect is not well known, but it is probably small.

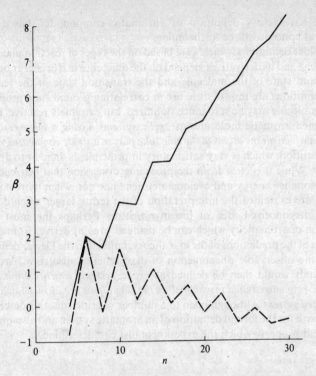

Figure 2.24 The delocalization energy (in β) calculated by the HMO (broken line) and Pople–Pariser–Parr (solid line) approximations for monocyclic conjugated systems (values for the PPP method taken from Dewar and Gleicher, *J. Am. Chem. Soc.*, 1965, **87**, 685).

2.6 Defining aromaticity

Of the three compounds that have been discussed in this chapter, benzene is the archetypal aromatic molecule and cyclooctatetraene may be taken as the typical non-aromatic molecule. Benzene is the prototype of the Hückel $(4n + 2)$ π-electron type, and cyclooctatetraene that of the $4n$ π-electron type, and these compounds support a possible classification scheme based on the Hückel Rule. A suitable definition on this basis would be that *aromatic systems are monocarbocyclic, conjugated molecules containing $(4n + 2)$ out-of-plane π-electrons*. Such a definition would have the merit that all of the terms can be precisely defined. However, it would have the disadvantage that many of the compounds normally considered to be aromatic, such as thiophene, pyridine, and naphthalene would be excluded. As will be discussed in chapter 3, problems also arise in monocyclic systems, both with regard to non-bonded interactions and the upper limit on the size of the ring, and so restrictions would also have to be put on the value of n. It is probable that no satisfactory definition of 'aromatic compounds' based on a structural concept will be forthcoming.

The older definitions, which were based on the types of reaction undergone by benzene and its derivatives, depend on the difference in free energy between the ground state of the molecule and the transition state of the reaction. Such definitions are thus of little use in correlating ground state properties, since a molecule may be resonance stabilized, but extremely reactive. Dewar has defined aromatic molecules as *cyclic systems having a large resonance energy in which all the atoms in the ring take part in a single conjugated system.* This definition, which is very satisfactory in principle, is difficult to apply in practice. While it is clear from the preceding discussion that benzene has a large resonance energy and cyclooctatetraene has not, when more complex systems are examined the interpretation of the term 'large' often depends on the preconceived idea of the investigator. Perhaps the most useful definition of aromaticity which can be made at present derives from a combination of the predictions of the m.o. theory, implicit in the Dewar definition, and in the observable phenomenon of diamagnetic anisotropy. Aromatic compounds would then be defined as *cyclic systems which exhibit a diamagnetic ring current and in which all of the ring atoms are involved in a single conjugated system.* Although open to a number of criticisms, this description allows both for the formal definition of an aromatic system and also provides a physical property which the experimentalist can determine.

Further reading

Many of the references given at the end of chapter 1 are also relevant to the present chapter. Discussions of the molecular orbital theory will be found in the texts of Dewar, Salem, and Streitweiser. The application of this theory to spectra is discussed in the following texts:

C. Sandorfy, *Electronic Spectra and Quantum Chemistry*, Prentice-Hall, 1964.

G. W. King, *Spectroscopy and Molecular Structure*, Holt, Reinehart and Winston, 1964.

J. N. Murrell, *The Theory of the Electronic Spectra of Organic Molecules*, Methuen, 1963.

The text by Sandorfy contains a clear description of the application of Group Theory to the classification of electronic states.

For a detailed discussion of the 255 nm absorption band of benzene see J. H. Callomon, T. M. Dunn, and I. M. Mills, *Phil. Trans. A.*, 1966, **259**, 60. The chemistry of cyclooctatetraene is reviewed by G. Schröder in *Cyclooctatetraene*, Verlag Chemie, 1965.

For an account of the chemistry of cyclobutadiene see the papers by P. Reeves, J. Hemery, and R. Pettit, in *J. Am. Chem. Soc.*, 1969, **91**, 5888, and by

P. Reeves, T. Devon, and R. Pettit, in *J. Am. Chem. Soc.*, 1969, **91**, 5890, and the references therein.

For a general review of the chemistry to be found in this and a number of the succeeding chapters, see P. J. Garratt and M. V. Sargent, ' Nonbenzenoid Conjugated Cyclic Hydrocarbons ', in *Advances in Organic Chemistry*, Volume 6, Interscience, 1969.

3. The annulenes

Cyclobutadiene, benzene, and cyclooctatetraene are members of an homologous series of fully conjugated monocyclic hydrocarbons of general formula $(C_2H_2)_n$. Such systems have been termed *annulenes*, and a prefixed number, [n], added to indicate the ring size. In this nomenclature benzene becomes [6]annulene, and cyclooctatetraene [8]annulene.

The annulenes have been the subject of a number of theoretical discussions, and one of the early successes of the m.o. theory was to explain the change in chemical properties on going from benzene to cyclooctatetraene (see chapter 2). Hückel's Rule predicts that those monocyclic hydrocarbons with $(4n + 2)$ π-electrons will have properties similar to those of benzene, whereas those with $4n$ π-electrons will exhibit properties similar to cyclooctatetraene. However, this rule does not consider geometrical factors, and Mislow pointed out that steric interactions would be particularly important in planar medium ring compounds in which the bond angle deformations have been minimized. Thus, in the planar, di-*trans* form of [10]annulene (1) acute interaction occurs between the inner hydrogens on the *trans* double bonds. Mislow predicted that [30]annulene (3) would be the first annulene

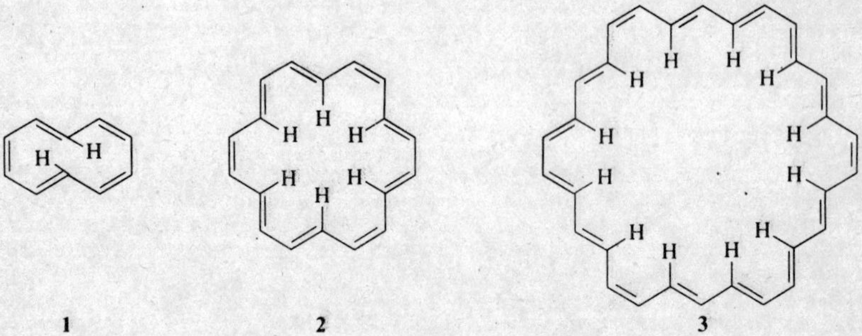

Figure 3.1

after benzene which could attain a sufficiently planar conformation for the π-electrons to be delocalized. Subsequently, other authors suggested that Mislow had over-estimated the steric requirements, and they proposed that the internal hydrogen interactions in [18]annulene (**2**) might be sufficiently small for this system to exhibit aromatic properties (Fig. 3.1).

Besides the question of steric interactions, a later theoretical treatment by Longuet–Higgins and Salem indicated that as the ring size increases the difference in energy between the delocalized and localized bond configuration models decreases, until in the region of rings containing 30 carbon atoms the system with localized bonds becomes energetically favoured. Thus, in the larger rings the difference between the $4n$ and $(4n + 2)$ π-electron annulenes disappears, and the larger annulenes would be expected to have properties similar to acyclic polyenes rather than to those of the smaller annulenes. Dewar and Gleicher later predicted that configurations with localized bonds would be favoured for the annulenes with more than 22 carbon atoms (see chapter 2).

In order to provide an experimental test of these predictions, Sondheimer and his collaborators began, in 1956, to investigate the preparation of a number of annulenes. The general procedure of the Sondheimer group is illustrated by their synthesis of [18]annulene (Fig. 3.2). The first step in the synthesis involves the oxidative coupling of a α,ω-diacetylene, which, besides linear products, gives cyclic ' monomers ', ' dimers ', ' trimers ', and higher cyclic ' oligomers '.* The total amount of cyclic products, and

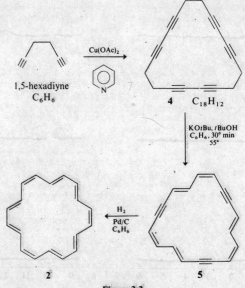

Figure 3.2

* All of these cyclic compounds are actually *not* ' oligomers ', having for each acetylene coupling two hydrogens *less* than the uncoupled starting materials.

relative proportions of the rings of various sizes depends upon the nature of the monomer and the reaction conditions used. The coupling reactions may be carried out under either Glaser conditions (oxygen in the presence of cuprous chloride and ammonium chloride) or Eglinton conditions (cupric acetate in pyridine). With the correctly chosen α,ω-diynes the resulting cyclic products on treatment with a strong base (usually potassium t-butoxide in t-butanol) are rearranged to the fully conjugated dehydroannulenes. In the case of the rearrangement of the $C_{18}H_{12}$ 'trimer' **4** (Fig. 3.2) three dehydro[18]annulenes were obtained; two of these were isomeric with the 'trimer', and one was an oxidation product containing two fewer hydrogens.

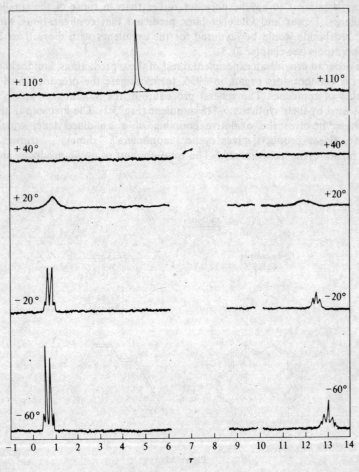

Figure 3.3 Nmr spectra of [18]annulene taken at 60 MHz at various temperatures in perdeuterotetrahydrofuran

Such dehydrogenations have been found to occur frequently during this type of rearrangement. In Fig. 3.2 only the major monocyclic product, 1,7,13-tridehydro[18]annulene (5) is shown. Partial hydrogenation of the dehydro[18]annulenes over palladium on charcoal gave crystalline [18]-annulene, as reddish-brown needles, having a main electronic maximum at 369 nm (ε 303,000).

[18]Annulene is a $(4n + 2)$ π-electron system, and should, by Hückel's Rule, be aromatic. The nmr spectrum (Fig. 3.3) in perdeuterotetrahydrofuran at 20° shows two broad bands at τ 1·06 and τ 12·0, which integrate for 12 and 6 protons respectively. This is the spectrum expected for an aromatic, delocalized π-electron system with 12 outer and 6 inner protons which is diamagnetically anisotropic. The spectrum was unexpectedly poorly resolved, the broad lines showing no fine structure, but these features were explained after it was realized that the spectrum is temperature dependent. At $-60°$ the spectrum (Fig. 3.3) exhibits multiplets at τ 0·72 and τ 12·99, consistent with an $A_{12}X_6$ system. At $+110°$, however, only a single resonance line was observed at τ 4·55, indicating that at this temperature the inner and outer protons have become equivalent. The molecule is thought to consist of three nearly planar conformational forms which are interconverting. The rate of interconversion at $-60°$ is sufficiently slow for discrete inner and outer protons signals to be observed, whereas at higher temperatures this rate increases until at 110° only an average position of the proton is seen in the nmr experiment (Fig. 3.4). Such an interpretation is supported by nmr

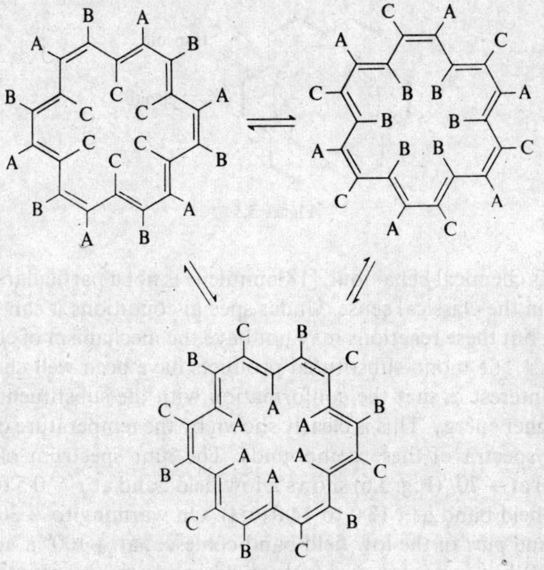

Figure 3.4

double irradiation experiments; thus, whereas at $-60°$ irradiation of the high field band causes the low field multiplet to collapse to a singlet, irradiation of the high field band at $20°$ causes the low field band to disappear. This is apparently due to the transfer of the irradiated inner protons to the position of outer protons before spin relaxation has occurred, which is equivalent to irradiating the outer protons.

The interchange of the internal and external protons in [18]annulene, which requires the equivalent of rotation around a carbon-carbon double bond, is a process of low activation energy (ca 14 kcal.mole^{-1}). The process possibly involves bond rotation and bond shift, similar to that described for cyclooctatetraene in chapter 2, but such a mechanism involves subtle arguments regarding the nature of delocalization.

It is of interest to point out that if the rotational barrier in [18]annulene had been a little smaller only a single resonance signal would have been observed at room temperature at a position (τ 4·55) more typical of a cyclooctatetraene type olefin than of benzene. Such a misleading observation was made with [14]annulene, which was thought at first to be a non-aromatic compound on the basis of the single resonance in the nmr spectrum.

A three-dimensional X-ray crystallographic analysis of [18]annulene showed that it was a nearly planar molecule, and that it did not have alternate single and double bonds. Two types of bonds were discerned, however, the ' cisoid ' type (1·419 Å) and the ' transoid ' type (1·382 Å), but these are not alternate. The structure of [18]annulene is best represented by Fig. 3.5.

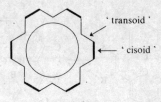

Figure 3.5

As regards chemical behaviour, [18]annulene is not a particularly aromatic compound in the classical sense. Under special conditions it can be nitrated or acylated, but these reactions may not have the mechanism of electrophilic substitutions. The mono-substituted products have been well characterized and are of interest in that the conformation with the substituent inside the ring is of higher energy. This is clearly shown by the temperature dependence of the nmr spectra of these compounds. The nmr spectrum of nitro[18]-annulene (**6**) at $-70°$ (Fig. 3.6) shows a low field band at $\tau - 0·5$ to $0·7$ (11H) and a high field band at τ 13·0 to 14·0 (6H). On warming to $+30°$, the high field band and *part* of the low field band coalesce; at $+100°$ a new band at ca τ 6·7 (12H) has appeared, and a low field band remains at τ 1·2–1·8 (5H).

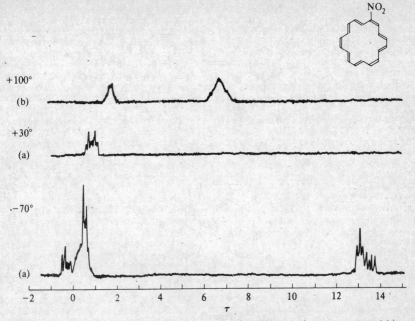

Figure 3.6 Nmr spectra of nitro[18]annulene taken at 100 MHz at various temperatures (a) in perdeuterotetrahydrofuran (b) in perdeuterotoluene.

It appears that, due to the higher energy of the conformation with an inner nitro group, the five protons associated with the nitro group *retain their distinct external character*, and only twelve of the protons show a temperature-dependent spectrum. The two interconverting conformations, together with the third non-contributing conformation, are shown in Fig. 3.7. In this figure, it is the five protons of type A which are external and temperature independent. These findings support the interpretation given above for the thermal behaviour of [18]annulene itself.

[18]Annulene reacts readily with bromine and maleic anhydride, reactions not expected for aromatic systems of the benzene type. It is, however, clear that the reaction pathways available to [18]annulene via rearrangement and valence tautomerism are considerably greater than those available to benzene, and the chemistry of the macrocyclic aromatic annulenes might be expected to differ from that of benzene in the same way that the chemistry of the macrocyclic alkene derivatives differs from the cyclohexene analogues.

One method of removing steric strain due to internal hydrogen atoms is to replace the hydrogens by a bridging atom or atoms. A number of such bridged [18]annulenes have been prepared by Badger and his co-workers. These workers used O, S, and N as 1,4-bridging groups, which also facilitated

Figure 3.7

the synthesis of the bridged [18]annulenes from five-membered heterocycles. Of the systems shown in Fig. 3.8, the compounds with three bridging oxygen atoms, or two bridging oxygen atoms and a sulphur atom have spectroscopic

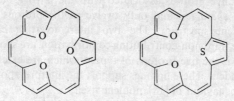

18 π-electron systems

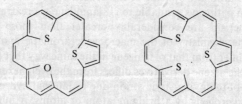

bridged heterocyclic systems

Figure 3.8

properties resembling [18]annulene. However, those with three bridging sulphur atoms, or two bridging sulphur atoms and an oxygen atom, have spectroscopic properties resembling the constituent heterocyclic systems. The difference in behaviour of these compounds may be due to two effects, the increased size of the sulphur atom and the greater aromaticity of thiophene compared to furan. It appears likely that the size of the atoms is more important, and these findings may indicate that if the system is distorted greatly from planarity, π-electron delocalization cannot occur.

[16]Annulene (7) was originally synthesized by Sondheimer and Gaoni by a route similar to that used for [18]annulene, but a superior synthesis has more recently been described by Schröder and Oth starting from the dimer (8) of cyclooctatetraene. Both of these synthetic schemes are shown in Fig. 3.9. The same configurational isomer of [16]annulene (7a), a brown crystalline compound, with a main ultraviolet maximum at 284 nm (ε 75,000), was obtained by either route. This is not unexpected as the barrier to rotational interconversion of the internal and external protons in [16]annulene is low (ca 9 kcal.mole^{-1}), and the adoption of the thermodynamically most stable configuration from any initial configuration is to be expected.

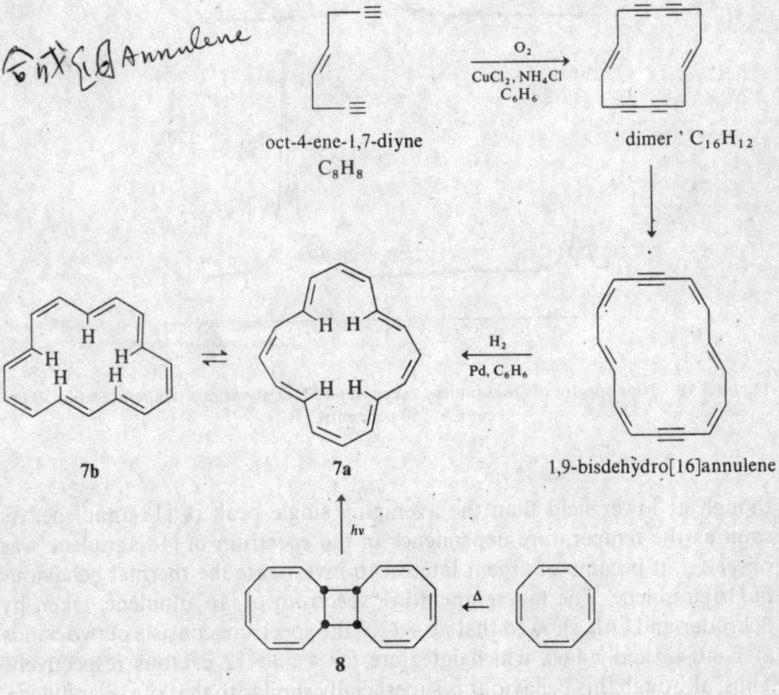

oct-4-ene-1,7-diyne
C_8H_8

' dimer ' $C_{16}H_{12}$

7b   7a   1,9-bisdehydro[16]annulene

8

Figure 3.9

51

[16]Annulene is a $4n$ π-electron system and thus should not, according to Hückel's Rule, be aromatic. The nmr spectrum (Fig. 3.10) taken at 35°, shows a single peak at τ 3·27 at a reasonable position for a cyclic olefin,

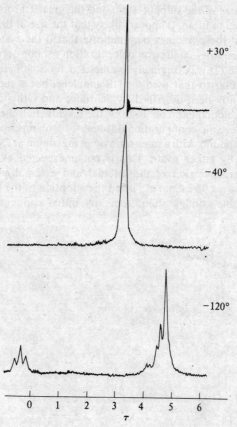

Figure 3.10   Nmr spectra of [16]annulene taken at 60 MHz at various temperatures in 50 per cent CS_2, 50 per cent $CDCl_2$.

though at lower field than the averaging single peak of [18]annulene. As soon as the temperature dependence of the spectrum of [18]annulene was observed, it became of urgent interest to investigate the thermal behaviour of [16]annulene. The low temperature spectrum of [16]annulene, taken by Schröder and Oth, showed that at −120° the spectrum consists of two bands at τ −0·43 and τ 4·60, which integrate for 4 and 12 protons respectively. Thus, although this behaviour is superficially similar to that of [18]annulene, the integration shows that in [16]annulene the *inner* protons are at *low* field, and the *outer* protons are at *high* field. This complete reversal of the position of the protons in the $4n$ compared to the $4n + 2$ annulenes has been explained as being due to the superimposition of a *paramagnetic* ring current upon the diamagnetic moment of the $4n$ π-electron systems. This paramagnetic ring current arises from the mixing of electronically excited states with the ground state of the $4n$ π-electron system. This interaction is magnetic-dipole allowed, and the resulting paramagnetic current should be large, because the difference in energy between the highest occupied and lowest unoccupied m.o. is small. In the $(4n + 2)$ π-electron annulenes this effect is small, as the states concerned have considerably different energies, and the transition between them is magnetic-dipole forbidden. The occurrence of a paramagnetic ring current was not observed in cyclooctatetraene, presumably because the molecule is far from planar, but as will be seen, the higher $4n$ annulenes up to and including [24]annulene exhibit this effect.

An X-ray single crystal structure analysis of [16]annulene shows that the molecule has alternate double and single bonds, and is significantly non-planar, although the deviation from planarity is not large. The four inner protons are arranged alternately on opposite sides of the mean molecular plane, thus minimizing the hydrogen–hydrogen interactions.

In solution [16]annulene has been shown to exist mainly as the isomer **7a**, but this is in equilibrium with a small amount of the configurational isomer **7b**. The interconversion **7a ⇌ 7b** occurs by a combination of a *cis-trans* isomerism similar to that in [18]annulene, together with a bond alternation process similar to that which occurs in cyclooctatetraene. A similar interconversion of isomers has also been observed in [12]annulene.

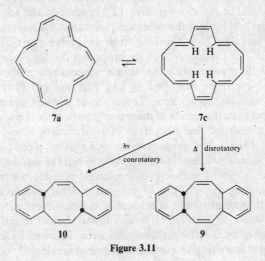

Figure 3.11

53

At the present time little is known of the chemistry of [16]annulene, and no attempts at electrophilic substitution have been reported. [16]Annulene valence isomerizes thermally via the conformational isomer **7c** to the tricyclic hydrocarbon **9**, and on photoirradiation gives the stereoisomer **10**, both reactions being orbital symmetry allowed (Fig. 3.11).

[16]- and [18]annulene are systems in which steric interactions are not excessively large, and in which a distinction between the $4n$ and $4n + 2$ type should still be clear. Although the properties of these systems are more complex and interesting than might have been expected initially, nevertheless the Hückel Rule does appear to be valid in predicting a difference in properties of the two classes of annulenes of this ring size. The problems may now be posed of the role of steric interaction in smaller annulenes and the limiting ring size for delocalization in the larger annulenes.

In planar [10]annulene the problem of steric strain is acute. Three planar configurational isomers of this system may be considered, the all-*cis* **11**, the mono-*trans* **12**, and the di-*trans* **1** configurations (Fig. 3.12). In the all-*cis*

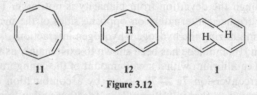

Figure 3.12

configuration **11** the bond angle strain is high (internal angle 144°), but there are no internal hydrogen-hydrogen interactions, whereas in the di-*trans* configuration **1** there is no bond angle strain, but the 1.6-hydrogens extensively interact. The mono-*trans* form **12** has some of the advantages (and disadvantages!) of both of the other configurations. Numerous attempts to prepare [10]annulene have shown it to be an elusive quarry, but it can be affirmed with full confidence that its properties do not resemble those of benzene. At the present time the closest approaches to the synthesis of [10]annulene are those described by van Tamelen and Burkoth, and by Masamune and his co-workers. There are at present some unresolved differences between the results of these two groups of workers. van Tamelen and Burkoth reported that photolysis of a solution of *trans*-9,10-dihydronaphthalene (**13**) at − 190° gave, on warming, a number of products including *cis*-9,10-dihydronaphthalene (**14**) (Fig. 3.13). When the solution was treated with di-imide prior to warming at the lowest possible temperature conducive to reaction (*ca* − 70°), a 40 per cent yield of cyclodecane (**15**) was obtained. These results were consistent with the formation of either all-*cis* (**11**) or di-*trans* [10]annulene (**1**) by an allowed photochemical conrotatory ring opening of *trans*-9,10-dihydronaphthalene, followed by a disrotatory thermal ring closure to give *cis*-9,10-dihydronaphthalene.

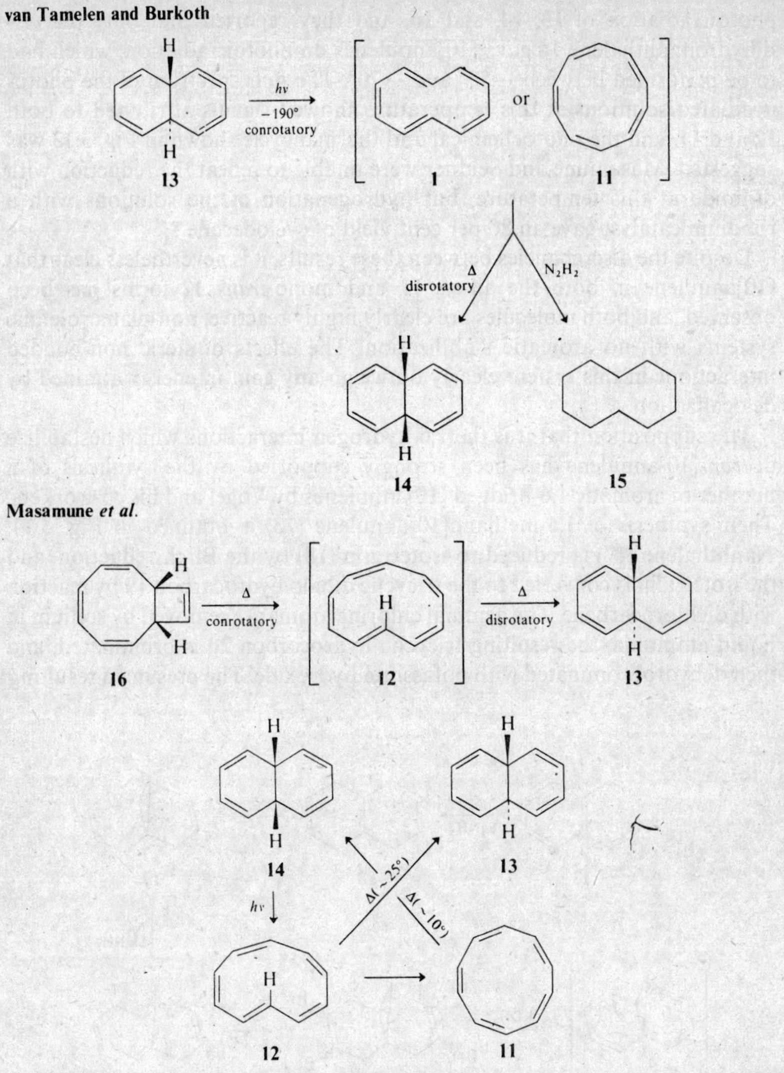

van Tamelen and Burkoth

Masamune *et al.*

Figure 3.13

Masamune and his co-workers originally observed that bicyclo[6.2.0]-deca-2,4,6,9-tetraene (**16**) is thermally rearranged to *trans*-9,10-dihydro-naphthalene (**13**), possibly via a conrotatory thermal ring opening to mono-trans[10]annulene (**12**), followed by a disrotatory ring closure to **13** (Fig. 3.13). In a subsequent publication, Masamune and Seidner examined the photoirradiation of **13**, **14**, and **16**, and they reported that only the *cis*-dihydronaphthalene **14** gave [10]annulenes on photoirradiation, which had to be performed between −50° and −70°. The nmr spectrum of the photo-irradiated solutions at this temperature showed signals attributed to both **12** and **11**, and the photochemical and thermal cycle shown in Fig. 3.13 was suggested. Masamune and Seidner were unable to repeat the reduction with di-imide at this temperature, but hydrogenation of the solutions with a rhodium catalyst gave an 80 per cent yield of cyclodecane.

Despite the discrepancies between these results, it is nevertheless clear that [10]annulene in both the all-*cis* **11** and mono-*trans* **12** forms has been observed, and both molecules are clearly highly reactive, non-planar olefinic systems with no aromatic stabilization. The effects of steric non-bonded interactions in this system clearly outweigh any gain in energy attained by delocalization.

The supposition that it is the 1,6-hydrogen interactions which destabilize di-*trans*[10]annulene has been strongly supported by the synthesis of a number of aromatic 1,6-bridged [10]annulenes by Vogel and his co-workers. Their synthesis of 1,6-methano[10]annulene (**23**) is outlined in Fig. 3.14. Naphthalene (**17**) is reduced to isotetralin (**18**) by the Birch reduction, and the isotetralin is converted to the tricyclic dihalo hydrocarbon **19** by reaction with dichlorocarbene. The geminal chlorine atoms are removed by sodium in liquid ammonia, the resulting tricyclic hydrocarbon **20** is brominated, and then dehydrobrominated with potassium hydroxide. The presumed resulting

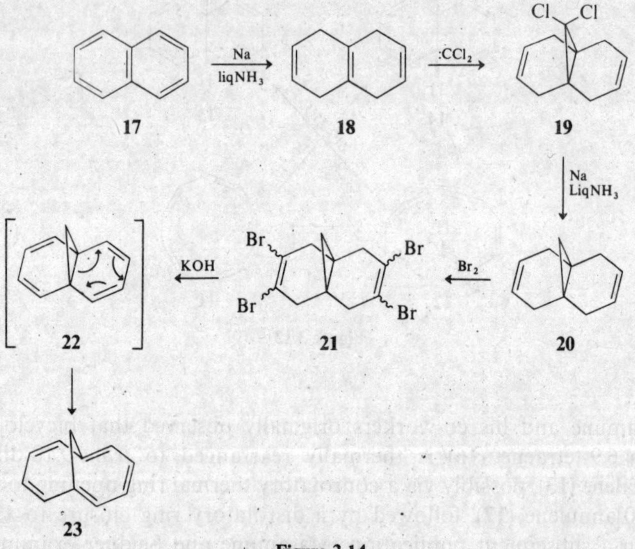

Figure 3.14

tricyclic intermediate **22** spontaneously valence tautomerizes to the aromatic bicyclic 1,6-methano[10]annulene (**23**).

The nmr spectrum of 1,6-methano[10]annulene has two bands, an A_4B_4 signal at τ 2·9, due to the ring protons, and a singlet at τ 10·5 due to the methylene bridge protons. This spectrum is consistent with either the tricyclic system or with the delocalized bicyclic system, but is not consistent with a bond localized bicyclic structure. The chemical shift position of the vinylic protons and the methylene bridge $^{13}C-H$ coupling constant, favours the delocalized, bicyclic 1,6-methano[10]annulene structure and the ultraviolet spectrum is also more in accord with **23**.

An X-ray crystallographic analysis of 1,6-methano[10]annulene-2-carboxylic acid (**24**) (Fig. 3.15) confirmed the delocalized structure, having a reasonably flat perimeter with non-alternating ' benzenoid ' type bonds (1·38–1·42 A).

Chemically, 1,6-methano[10]annulene is a stable compound, insensitive to oxygen and heat, not polymerizing easily, and it does not form an adduct with maleic anhydride in boiling benzene. At higher temperatures an adduct is formed with maleic anhydride, the structure of which is derived from the tricyclic valence tautomer. 1,6-Methano[10]annulene undergoes an apparent

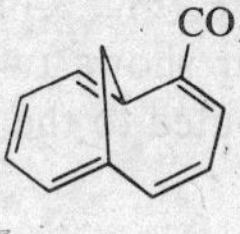

24

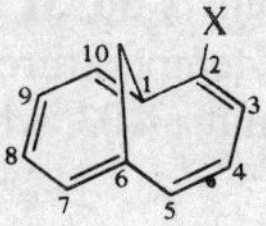

25a X = Br
25b X = COCH$_3$
25c X = NO$_2$

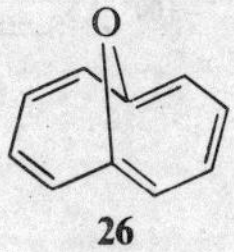

26

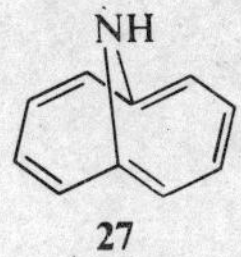

27

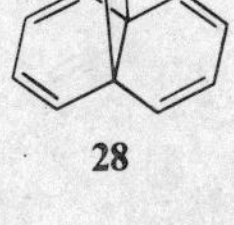

28

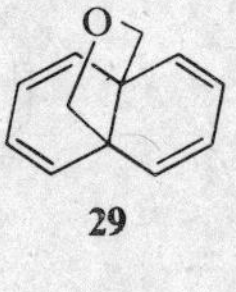

29

Figure 3.15

electrophilic substitution with bromine or N-bromosuccinimide, but this may occur by an addition-elimination mechanism. Acylation occurs with acetic anhydride in the presence of stannic chloride, and nitration occurs with cupric nitrate in acetic anhydride. In all of these cases the substitution occurs in the 2-position to give the derivatives **25a–c** (Fig. 3.15).

Oxygen and nitrogen have also been utilized as the 1,6-bridging atom, and in both 1,6-oxido[10]annulene (**26**) and 1,6-imino[10]annulene (**27**) the macrocyclic ring is reasonably planar and exhibits aromatic properties (Fig. 3.15). However, when the 1,6-bridge contains more than one atom, as in 4a,8a-ethanonaphthalene (**28**) and 4a,8a-(methanoxymethano)naphthalene (**29**), the tricyclic, nondelocalized structure is more stable (Fig. 3.15). It thus appears in these compounds that there is a balance between the delocalized bicyclic and the tricyclic systems. In the cases with one-atom bridges, the tricyclic structure is probably destabilized due to the possession of the double norcaradiene system, and this facilitates ring opening to the delocalized, bicyclic [10]annulene (Fig. 3.15).

A number of benzannelated [10]annulenes have recently been synthesized, having two or more fused benzene rings. All of these show spectroscopic and chemical properties consistent with the 10-membered ring possessing a buckled, non-planar conformation with localized double bonds. The stability of these compounds compared to [10]annulene may be partially due to the benzene rings preventing ready valence tautomerism.

[12]Annulene (**33**) has recently been prepared by photoirradiation of one of its valence tautomers **30, 31** or **32** at −100° (Fig. 3.16). The molecule is only stable at low temperature, and the nmr shows two signals of equal intensity at τ 3·12 and τ 4·03, which are attributed to the protons on the *cis*

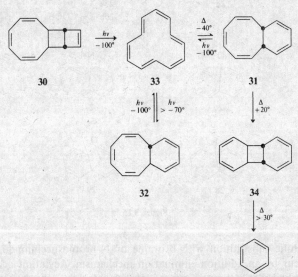

Figure 3.16

and *trans* double bonds respectively. The equivalence of these protons is due to the rapid conformational interconversion of **33a** and **33b** (Fig. 3.17), which has a low activation energy ($\Delta G = 5.5$ kcal.mole^{-1}), presumably due to the overcrowding of the hydrogens in the centre of the ring. The bond shift process does not appear to occur at this temperature. The chemical shifts of the protons suggest that [12]annulene has only a small paramagnetic ring current.

At $-40°$, [12]annulene rearranges to the bicyclic tautomer **31**, which at $+20°$ undergoes further rearrangement to **34**. The compound **34** on photo-irradiation or heating above 30° gives benzene. These rearrangements of **33** to **31** and **32** and the reverse reactions are not allowed by the rules of orbital symmetry, and it is presumed that in [12]annulene the configuration **33** is in equilibrium with a small amount of the configuration **35** (Fig. 3.17). This interconversion is a process similar to that discussed for [16]annulene, and the rearrangements of **35** are orbital symmetry allowed.

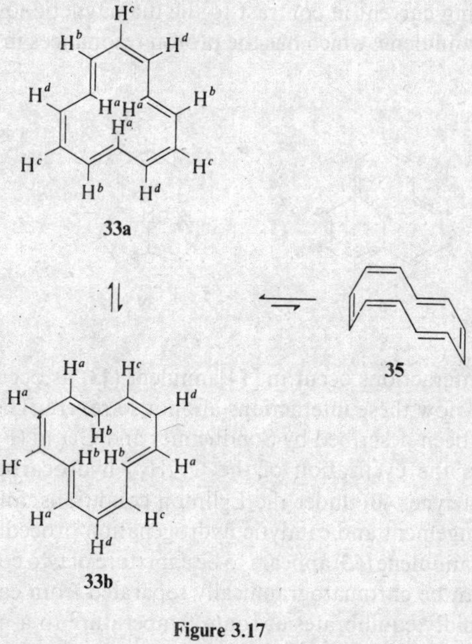

33a

35

33b

Figure 3.17

Two dehydro[12]annulenes have been synthesized, 1,5,9-tridehydro-[12]annulene (**36**) and 1,5-bisdehydro[12]annulene (**37a**). The nmr spectra of these compounds indicate that they both possess paramagnetic ring currents, and this is dramatically emphasized by the spectrum of 9-bromo-1,5-bisdehydro[12]annulene (**37b**), in which the inner proton is at τ -6.4!

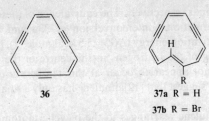

36

37a R = H
37b R = Br

A tribenzo[12]annulene and a number of benzannelated dehydro[12]-annulenes have been prepared. The spectroscopic properties of the tribenzo-1,5,9-tridehydro[12]annulene are indicative of a planar system.

Cycl[3,3,3]azine (**38**), a bridged [12]annulene, has recently been synthesized by Farquhar and Lever. This compound, which is a brown crystalline solid, shows in the nmr spectrum the expected A_2B, pattern consisting of a triplet at τ 6·35 due to protons 2, 5, and 8, with a doublet at τ 7·93 for the remaining six protons. The high field positions of these signals indicate that **38** sustains a paramagnetic ring current in contrast to the diamagnetic lower analogue **39**, a bridged [10]annulene, which has the proton resonances in the aromatic region (τ 2·1–2·8).

38

39

Similar steric interactions occur in [14]annulene (**43**) as occur in [10] and [12]annulene, but now these interactions are not so severe. The synthesis of [14]annulene has been described by Sondheimer and Gaoni (Fig. 3.18). This synthesis involves the cyclization of the $C_{14}H_{14}$ hydrocarbon tetradeca-4,10-diene-1,7,13-triyne (**40**) under the Eglinton conditions, followed by the usual base rearrangement and catalytic hydrogenation procedure.

In solution [14]annulene (**43**) appears to be a mixture of two configurational isomers, which can be chromatographically separated from each other, but each of which rapidly equilibrates at room temperature to a mixture of the two isomers. Crystalline [14]annulene is the pure, major component of the isomeric mixture, and a preliminary X-ray analysis indicated that the molecule is near planar, centrosymmetric and of the configuration shown by **43**. The nmr spectrum of the major isomer of [14]annulene at room temperature showed only a single band at τ 4·42, but on cooling this band disappeared, and on further cooling to $-60°$ two new bands appeared at τ 2·4 (10H) and τ 10·0 (4H) due to the outer and inner protons, respectively. [14]Annulene is

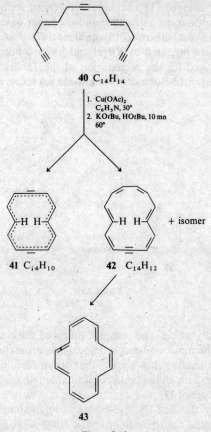

40 $C_{14}H_{14}$

1. $Cu(OAc)_2$
   C_6H_5N, 50°
2. $KOtBu$, $HOtBu$, 10 mn
   60°

41 $C_{14}H_{10}$ **42** $C_{14}H_{12}$ + isomer

43

Figure 3.18

thus showing the same behaviour as [18]annulene, except that in this case the barrier to proton-interchange is lower (*ca* 11 kcal.mole^{-1}), and a time averaged spectrum is observed at room temperature.

1,8-Bisdehydro[14]annulene (**41**) has an nmr spectrum consisting of three bands, two at low field (τ 0·36, τ 1·46), and one at very high field (τ 15·48), due to the outer and inner protons respectively. The magnitude of the chemical shift indicates the presence of a large, diamagnetic ring current. 1,8-Bisdehydro[14]annulene also exhibits classical aromatic properties, and a number of derivatives have been prepared by electrophilic substitution reactions. A mixture of two monodehydro[14]annulene is also produced during the course of the [14]annulene synthesis, one of which has the structure **42**.

Two types of bridged [14]annulenes have been reported, the one type based on the ' anthracene ' structure and the other based on the ' pyrene ' structure. *Syn*-1,6:8,13-Bisoxido[14]annulene (47) is of the ' anthracene ' type, and has been prepared by Vogel and his co-workers by a route very similar to that used for the preparation of the 1,6-bridged [10]annulenes (Fig. 3.19). *Syn*-1,6:8,13-Bisoxido[14]annulene is a red, crystalline compound

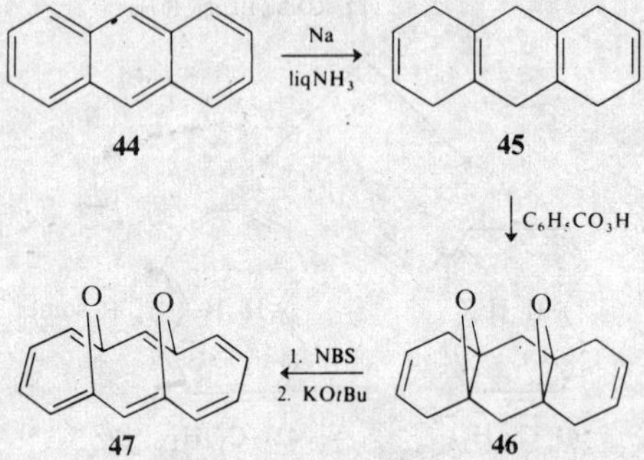

Figure 3.19

which is thermally stable. The complex nmr and the electronic spectra are in accord with the molecule being a delocalized, aromatic system. An X-ray crystallographic analysis has shown that the molecule has a reasonably planar perimeter, with all the bonds of similar length (*ca* 1·39 Å), supporting the aromatic nature of 47.

More recently the *anti*-1,6:8,13-bismethano[14]annulene (48) has been prepared, and found not to be an aromatic compound, presumably because orbital overlap is hindered in this configuration. The compound 48 does undergo band shift (48a ⇌ 48b), however, possibly via a delocalized transition state, in a similar manner to cyclooctatetraene (chapter 2). In

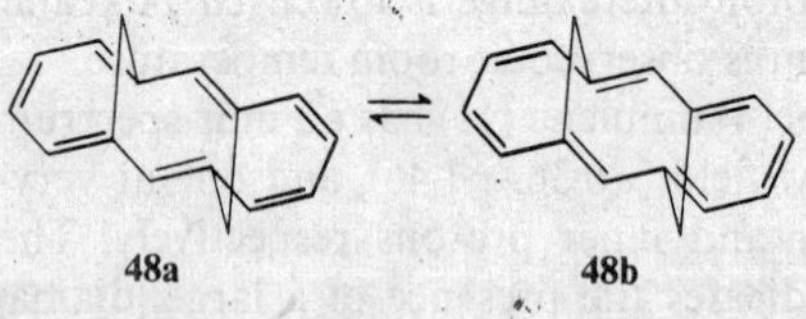

contrast the bridged methano[14]annulene (49) is an aromatic compound, the protons on the bridge atoms appearing at high field in the nmr spectrum (τ 10·61–11·16) with the ring protons at low field (τ 2·12–2·36). The X-ray crystallographic analysis indicates that 49 has a very similar geometry to

47. Attempts to prepare *syn*-1,6:8,13-bismethano[14]annulene **(50)** failed, presumably due to the non-bonded interactions of the bridge atoms, which are removed in compound **49**. A number of other related systems have also been prepared.

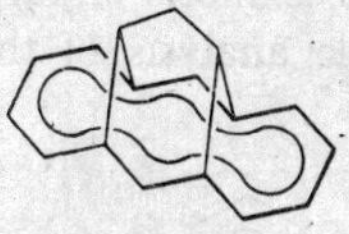

Mitchell and Boekelheide have prepared *trans*-15,16-dihydropyrene **(56)**, a [14]annulene with a central ethano bridge which is based on the pyrene system. The synthetic sequence is shown in Fig. 3.20, and the key reaction is the extrusion of sulphur by the Stevens rearrangement (e.g., **53 → 54**). The compound **56** can only be formed in the presence of pyrene, but its physical properties are readily observed. The solutions of **56** in cyclohexane are deep green, and the nmr spectrum shows signals at τ 1·42 ($H^{4,5,9,10}$), 1·50 ($H^{1,3,6,8}$) and 1·98–2·11 ($H^{2,7}$), while the inner protons $H^{15,16}$ appear at τ 15·49. The high field signal of the inner protons confirms that **56** has a large

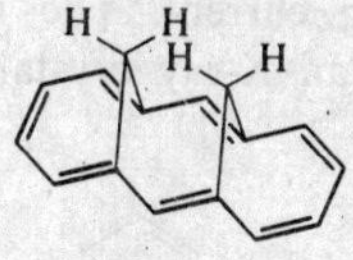

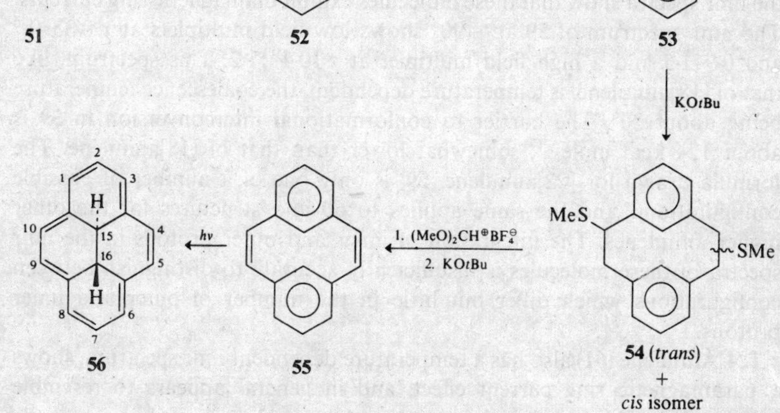

Figure 3.20

63

diamagnetic ring current. Boekelheide and Philips had earlier prepared *trans*-15,16-dimethyldihydropyrene (**57**), by a long synthetic route, and this compound is now more easily accessible via the Stevens rearrangement sequence. The compound **57** shows the ring proton absorptions at τ 1·33–2·02, and the internal methyl groups at τ 14·25, again indicative of a large diamagnetic ring current. The molecule exhibits a large diamagnetic anisotropy, and an X-ray crystallographic analysis of the 2,7-diacetoxy

57   **58**

derivative shows that the bond lengths do not alternate, varying between 1·386 and 1·401 Å. These properties are consistent with a delocalized, aromatic system. *trans*-15,16-Dimethyldihydropyrene undergoes a range of electrophilic substitution reactions, substitution occurring at position 2, and thus in both its chemical and physical properties it appears to be an aromatic compound. An interesting valence tautomerism occurs between **57** and the metacyclophane **58**; the metacyclophane is produced by photo-irradiation of **57** and reverts thermally to **57** at room temperature.

In the larger annulenes where the problem of steric interaction is much less, the question of bond localization now obtrudes. [22]Annulene (**59**) and monodehydro[22]annulene (**60**) have both recently been prepared, and the nmr spectra show that these molecules exhibit diamagnetic ring currents. The nmr spectrum of **59** at −90° shows low field multiplets at τ 0·35–0·7 and 0·9–1·5 and a high field multiplet at τ 10·4–11·2. This spectrum, like that of [18]annulene, is temperature dependent, the coalescence temperature being about 20°. The barrier to conformational interconversion in **59** is about 12·8 kcal mole^{-1}, somewhat lower than that of [18]annulene. The formula drawn for [22]annulene, **59**, is only one of a number of possible configurations, and the same applies to **60** and structures for the other higher annulenes. The integration of inner and outer protons in the nmr spectra of these molecules is insufficiently accurate to distinguish between configurations which differ but little in the number of outer and inner protons.

[24]Annulene (**61**) also has a temperature dependent nmr spectrum, shows a paramagnetic ring current effect, and in general appears to resemble [16]annulene. [26]Annulene has not been prepared, and until very recently

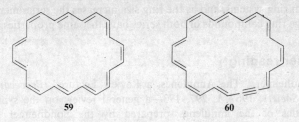

59   60

the only known derivative was a tridehydro[26]annulene, which had a localized bond structure and showed no diamagnetic ring current. A mono-dehydro[26]annulene (62) has, however, now been synthesized, and this

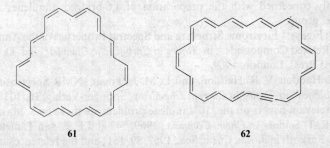

61   62

compound does show a diamagnetic ring current. [30]Annulene has been prepared, but its nmr spectrum was not studied. Two dehydro[30]annulenes have also been prepared, and the nmr spectra of these resemble, like tridehydro[26]annulene, the spectra of linear polyenynes rather than those of the smaller dehydroannulenes. It thus appears likely that somewhere between [24] and [30]annulene the bond localized structure becomes thermodynamically favoured over that with delocalized bonds, and the properties of the macrocyclic annulenes become independent of the number of π-electrons.

There are thus, beside benzene, a number of monocyclic conjugated carbocyclic compounds which have closed electronic shells and which have aromatic spectral properties. However, as would be predicted on theoretical grounds, these systems are chemically much more reactive, and show much less tendency to retain the closed electronic shell than benzene. Part of this increased reactivity may be attributed to the occurrence of transannular reactions, and this is borne out by the observation that it is the $4n + 2$ π-electron dehydroannulenes and bridged annulenes rather than the annulenes themselves, which more closely resemble benzene. Parallel with this series are the molecules with $4n$ π-electrons, having nonplanar conformations and exhibiting paramagnetic ring current effects. Both of these series are interrupted by the intrusion of steric factors which destabilize the

65

medium ring systems, and as the ring size increases the series merge, so that the large ring compounds of both series have the same properties.

Further reading

F. Sondheimer, ' The Annulenes, a Review Lecture ', *Proceedings of the Royal Society*, 1967 **A**, **297**, 173—a general review on the synthesis and properties of the annulenes prepared by the Sondheimer group. F. Sondheimer *et al.*, ' The Annulenes and Related Compounds ' in *Aromaticity, an International Symposium*, Chemical Society Special Publication, No. 21, 75 (1967)—nmr spectra of the annulenes and dehydroannulenes.

E. Vogel, ' Aromatic 10 π-electron Systems ' in *Aromaticity, an International Symposium*, Chemical Society Special Publication, No. 21, 113 (1967)—mainly concerned with the preparation of 1,6-bridged annulenes by the Vogel group.

H. P. Figeys, ' Electronic Structure and Spectral Properties of the Annulenes and Related Compounds ', in *Topics in Carbocyclic Chemistry*, ed. D. Lloyd, Logos Press, London, 1969.

R. C. Haddon, V. R. Haddon, and L. M. Jackman, 'NMR Spectroscopy of Annulenes', in *Topics in Current Chemistry*, Springer-Verlag, **16**, 103 (1971). The relevant papers on the [10]annulene problem are those by S. Masamune and R. T. Seidner in *Chem. Commun.*, 1969, 542 and E. E. van Tamelen and T. L. Burkoth in *J. Am. Chem. Soc.*, 1967, **89**, 151; and the references in these papers. An account of the general problem can be found in the article by van Tamelen and Burkoth in *Nonbenzenoid Aromatics*, ed. J. P. Snyder, Academic Press, New York, 1969. See also E. E. van Tamelen and R. H. Greeley, *Chem. Commun.*, 1971, 601.

For the synthesis of [12]annulene, see the papers by J. F. M. Oth, H. Röttele and G. Schröder in *Tetrahedron Letters*, 1970, 61, and by J. F. M. Oth, J.-M. Gilles and G. Schröder in *Tetrahedron Letters*, 1970, 67.

Accounts of the recent work in the bridged [14]annulene field, together with references to earlier work, will be found by E. Vogel *et al.*, *Angew. Chem. Int. Ed. Eng.*, 1970, **9**, 513, 514, 516, 517, and by R. H. Mitchell and V. Boekelheide, in *J. Am. Chem. Soc.*, 1970, **92**, 3510.

For recent work on the larger annulenes see the paper by R. M. McQuilkin, B. W. Metcalf, and F. Sondheimer, *Chem. Commun.*, 1971, 338, and references therein.

4. Monocyclic aromatic ions

The Hückel Rule predicts that conjugated monocyclic ions with $(4n + 2)$ π-electrons will be aromatic, whereas those with $4n$ π-electrons will not. A considerable amount of experimental work had been carried out prior to the enunciation of this rule, and many subsequent studies were made without reference to its predictions.

Thiele, in 1901, observed that when cyclopentadiene (1) is heated with a dispersion of potassium in benzene under nitrogen, potassium cyclopentadienide (2) is formed. In the same year he also noted that the similar treatment of cycloheptatriene (3) did not yield potassium cycloheptatrienide (4). The difference in acidity of the methylene groups in the two hydrocarbons can now be accounted for in terms of the stability of the resulting anions, since cyclopentadiene yields the aromatic, 6 π-electron cyclopentadienyl anion, whereas the cycloheptatrienyl anion has an unfilled shell of 8 π-electrons, and is not aromatic (Fig. 4.1).

At the time, Thiele suggested that the difference in behaviour of the two hydrocarbons might be due to a nonbonded interaction between the 1,6-carbon atoms of the cycloheptatriene, giving an aromatic structure, and thus deactivating the methylene group of 3 compared to that of 1. Although this interaction probably contributes little to the deactivation of cyclo-heptatriene, it is a pre-electronic concept corresponding to homoaromaticity, which is discussed further in chapter 9.

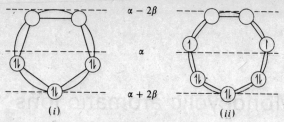

Figure 4.1 HMO energy levels of the cyclopentadienyl anion (i) and the cycloheptatrienyl anion (ii).

Prior to these experiments of Thiele, Merling, while carrying out an investigation on tropine, had observed that cycloheptatriene on bromination gave a dibromide as an oil, which, on attempted distillation, partially decomposed to give hydrogen bromide and a crystalline solid. With the formation of this solid Merling had prepared the first stable carbonium ion, cycloheptatrienium bromide (**5**), but not surprisingly, this was not recognized until much later, when these experiments were repeated by Doering and Knox in 1954. The cycloheptatrienium cation is predicted by the Hückel rule to be aromatic (Fig. 4.2).

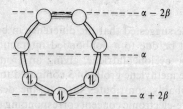

Between 1901 and 1945 the main advances in this area were of a theoretical nature, culminating in Hückel's prediction that the cycloheptatrienium cation would be a stable, aromatic system. Pfau and Plattner did prepare azulene (**6**), but this aroused more interest as the parent hydrocarbon of a number of natural products rather than as an aromatic system. Little attention

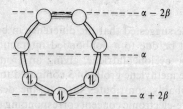

Figure 4.2

was paid to the Hückel predictions until Dewar, in 1945, postulated structures for stipitatic acid and colchicine which were based on a seven-membered

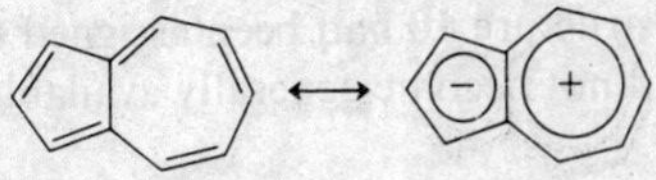

6a   6b

aromatic ring. In his first communication, using the published experimental results of Birkinshaw, Chambers, and Raistrick, Dewar suggested that stipitatic acid had the structure 7. He further postulated that there might be a family of aromatic systems in which hydrogen bonding gave structures analogous to azulene, and on this basis suggested the trivial name tropolone for the parent compound, cycloheptatrienolone (8). However, in the structure

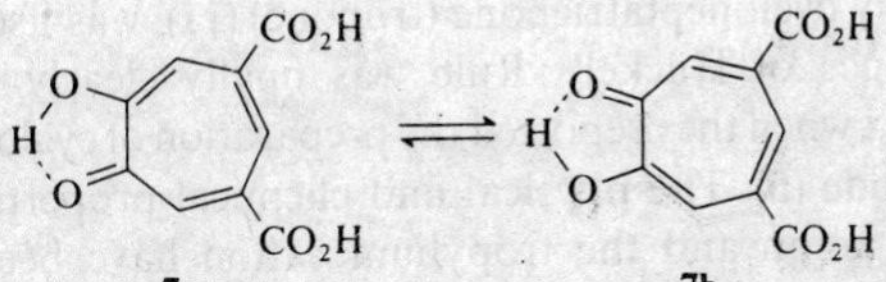

7a   7b

subsequently suggested for colchicine (9)† the tropolone ring occurs as the methyl ether, and hydrogen bonding can thus not be important in this structure. The stability of the tropolone ring was now considered to arise from the contribution of a dipolar structure (e.g., 8b), and the possibility was also advanced that tropolone might be a highly mobile tautomeric system.

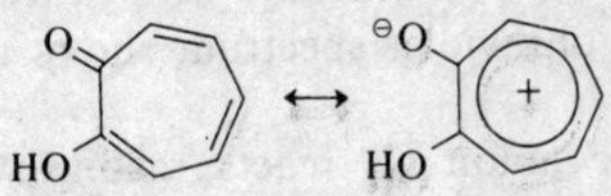

8a   8b

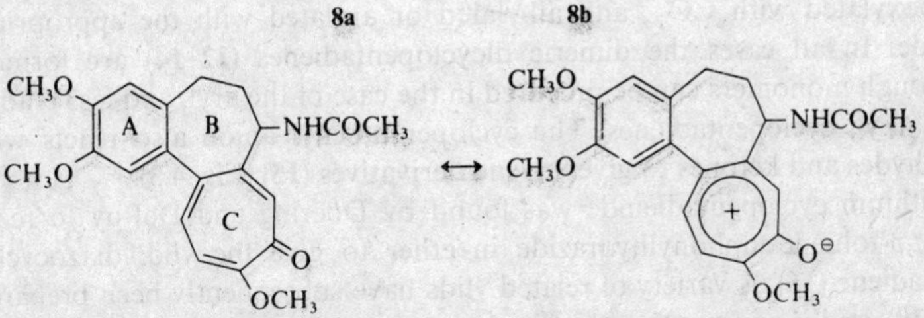

9a   9b

† In his suggested structure for colchicine, Dewar left open the actual orientation of ring C with respect to ring A. The structure shown is that subsequently demonstrated to be that of colchicine.

69

At the same time that Dewar was subjecting the literature to this remarkable analysis, Nozoe and his co-workers had arrived at similar conclusions regarding a natural product, hinokitiol, which they had isolated from the Formosan Cedar. The structure **10** had been assigned to hinokitiol, but an account of this work did not become generally available until 1951.

10   **11**

The structure suggested by Dewar for stipitatic acid was readily confirmed, and successful syntheses of the parent tropolone (**8**) were described shortly after. Subsequently cycloheptatrienone (tropone) (**11**), was itself synthesized, and the importance of Hückel's Rule was finally clearly enunciated by Doering and Knox when they reported the preparation of cycloheptatrienium (tropylium) bromide (**5**). The physical and chemical properties of both the cyclopentadienyl anion and the tropylium cation have been investigated in some detail.

The cyclopentadienyl anion can be prepared by treatment of cyclopentadiene with either alkali metals or alkali hydroxides. The magnetic and electrochemical properties of the salts formed in this manner indicate that these are ionic compounds. The infrared and Raman spectra of the ions are simple, as expected for a molecule of D_{5h} symmetry, and the nmr spectrum shows a single resonance at τ 4.43. The chemical shift of the protons is in reasonable agreement for a system with a diamagnetic ring current of the same magnitude as that of benzene and with $\frac{1}{5}$ excess electron density at each carbon atom. The ultraviolet spectrum shows no absorption above 200 nm.

The cyclopentadienide anion (**2**) reacts readily with electrophiles, is carboxylated with CO_2, and alkylated or arylated with the appropriate halide. In all cases the dimeric dicyclopentadienes (**12–14**) are formed, although monomers can be prepared in the case of the aryl, and less readily the alkyl, cyclopentadienes. The cyclopentadienyl anion also reacts with aldehydes and ketones to give fulvene derivatives (**15**) (Fig. 4.3).

Lithium cyclopentadienide was found by Doering and DePuy to react with *p*-toluenesulphonylhydrazide in ether to give the ylid, diazocyclopentadiene (**16**). A variety of related ylids have subsequently been prepared (**17–19**), and it appears that the dipolar structure (e.g., **16b**) is a major factor in stabilizing these compounds. All of these ylids have large dipole moments, for example that of triphenylphosphonium cyclopentadienylid (**19**) is 7·0D, and these values can be ascribed to the contribution of the dipolar form.

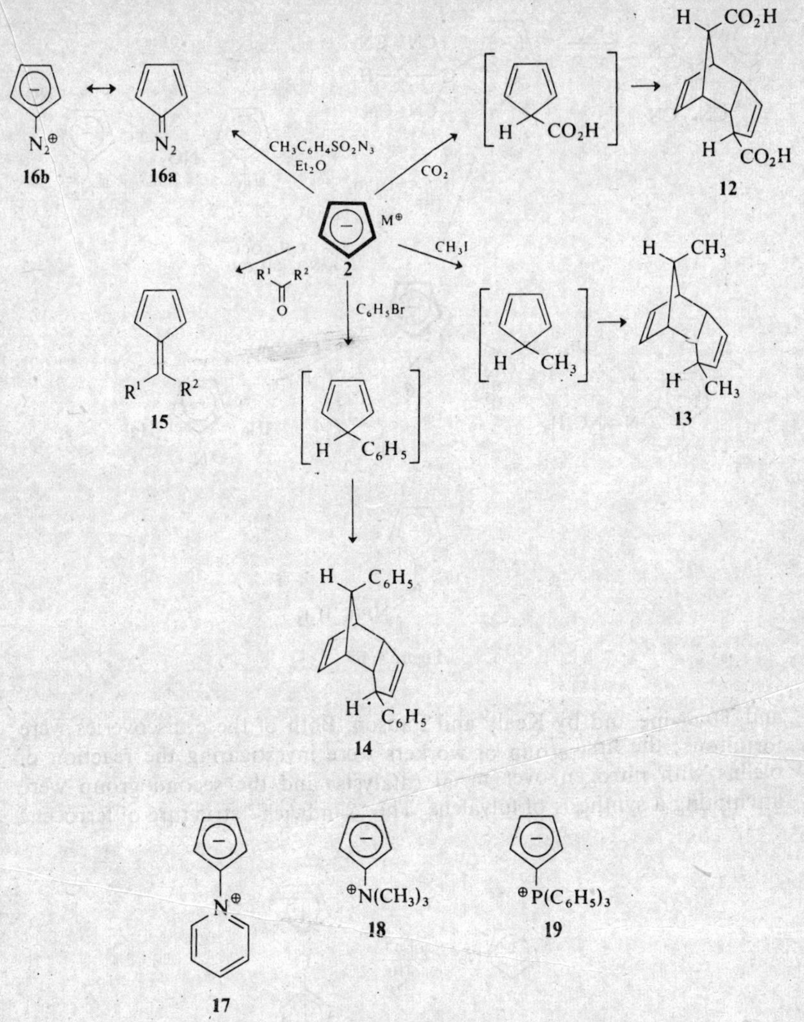

Figure 4.3

Both diazocyclopentadiene (**16**) and triphenylphosphonium cyclopenta-dienylid (**19**) undergo electrophilic substitution in the cyclopentadienyl ring, and some reactions of **16** are shown in Fig. 4.4.

The other reaction of importance of the cyclopentadienyl anion is with transition metal salts, which gives the organometallic 'sandwich' compounds, the metallocenes. The first compound of this type to be prepared was ferrocene (**20**), which was independently discovered by Miller, Tebboth,

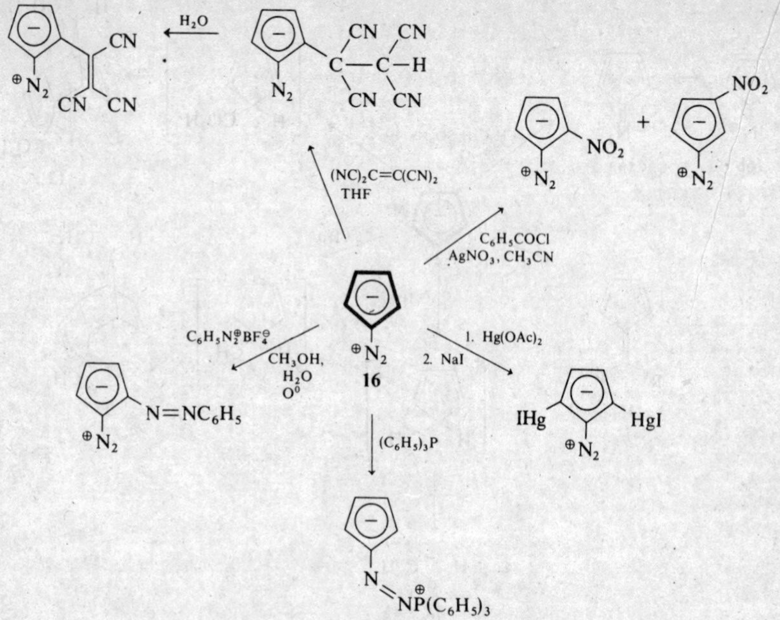

Figure 4.4

and Tremaine and by Kealy and Pauson. Both of these discoveries were fortuitous; the first group of workers were investigating the reaction of olefins with nitrogen over metal catalysts, and the second group were attempting a synthesis of fulvalene. The 'sandwich' structure of ferrocene

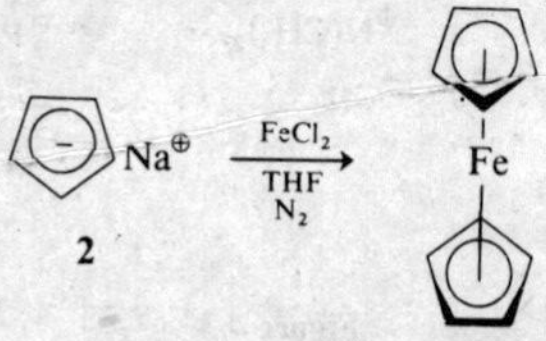

was first proposed by Wilkinson *et al.* shortly afterwards; a number of analogous compounds were soon reported, and the aromatic nature of ferrocene was demonstrated. The infrared spectrum shows only one type of C—H stretching mode, which is in accord with the symmetrical structure. An electron count of the ferrocene system, assuming a contribution of ten electrons from the cyclopentadienyl rings and eight electrons from the iron, gives the krypton inert gas structure to the complex. As expected for such a structure with no unpaired electrons, ferrocene is diamagnetic. Alternative extreme descriptions of the ferrocene system have been made in which the structure is considered to be either two cyclopentadienyl anions bonded to a dipositive ferrous iron atom, or in which essentially co-valent bonding occurs between the neutral cyclopentadienyl rings and a neutral iron atom. The latter description appears to be more appropriate to the chemistry of ferrocene, and a satisfactory series of molecular orbitals for bonding can be provided. In the early m.o. treatments most of the bonding was assumed to be derived from the lowering in energy caused by the mixing of the e_{1g} orbitals of the cyclopentadienyl rings with the $3d_{xy,yz}$ orbitals on the iron (Fig. 4.5). More sophisticated treatments suggest that twelve electrons of the eighteen

Figure 4.5 Overlap of the e_{1g} orbitals of the cyclopentadienyl rings (shown as p_π atomic orbitals) with the iron $3d_{xy,yz}$ orbitals in ferrocene.

available are involved in bonding, but there is considerable disagreement on the relative energies of the orbitals, and on the sign of the partial charge on the iron atom.

The chemistry of ferrocene reveals the aromatic nature of the compound. Friedel-Crafts acylation gives 1,1'-diacylferrocenes (**21**), while sulphonation gives ferrocene-1,1'-disulphonic acid (**22**).

In the crystalline state ferrocene has the cyclopentadienyl rings staggered as shown in formula **20**. The barrier to rotation of the rings is, however, low, and in solution or the vapour state free rotation occurs. This has been shown by both physical measurements, and by classical substitution studies. Thus the dipole moment for the diacetylferrocenes is in good agreement for a structure exhibiting free rotation, while acetylation of monoethyl ferrocene gives three isomeric acetylethyl ferrocenes, which were the three isomers expected if free rotation occurs. These isomers were **23** and **24**, with both substituents in the same ring, and **25** with the substituents in different rings. In contrast to ferrocene, ruthenocene and most of the other metallocenes have eclipsed cyclopentadienyl rings.

Attempts to nitrate or brominate ferrocene directly are frustrated in that it is the iron atom which is attacked, being oxidized from the ferrous to the ferric state to give the blue-green ferricenium ion (**26**). The ferricenium ion is paramagnetic and water soluble, in contrast to ferrocene, and the paramagnetic moment is consistent with the possession of an unpaired electron. The oxidation is reversible, and the ferricenium ion is readily reduced to ferrocene.

A voluminous chemistry of this type of sandwich compounds has been developed, which will not be discussed here, and the interested reader is directed to the relevant references at the end of this chapter.

The chemistry of the tropylium cation (**5**), has also been extensively developed. A summary of the methods of preparing **5** is shown in Fig. 4.6. The preferred methods of synthesis appear to be that due to Dauben and his co-workers, in which cycloheptatriene (**3**) is reacted with the trityl cation

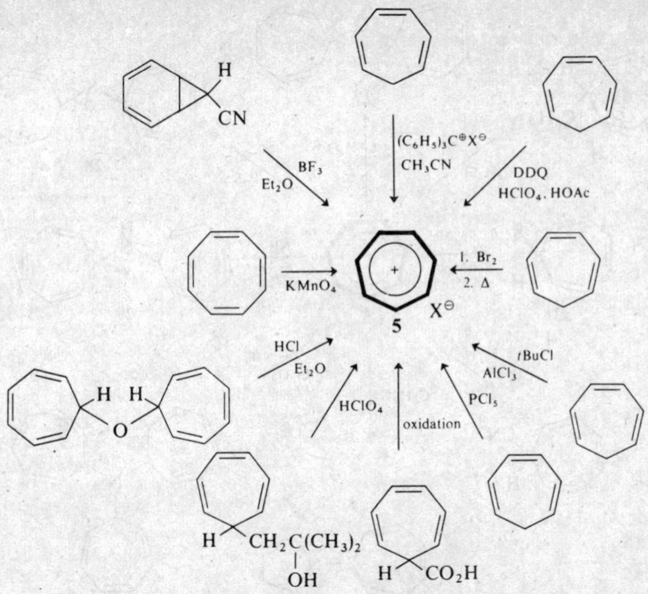

Figure 4.6

[(C_6H_5)$_3C^\oplus$], preferably as the perchlorate or tetrafluoroborate, in sulphur dioxide or acetonitrile, and that due to Conrow in which **3** is treated with PCl$_5$ in carbon tetrachloride.

The cation **5** shows the simple infrared and Raman spectra expected for the planar structure of D_{7h} symmetry, with no coincidence of the infrared and Raman bands. The nmr spectrum shows a singlet at τ 0·72, the position of the chemical shift being in good agreement with that calculated on the basis of the benzene ring current and $\frac{1}{7}$ of a positive charge on each carbon atom. The ultraviolet spectrum has an absorption maximum at 275 nm, in reasonable agreement with that calculated, 287 nm. The cation has a pK$_a$ of 4·01, and thus has a comparable acidity in water to acetic acid.

The tropylium cation reacts as an electrophile, and its reaction with a variety of nucleophiles is shown in Fig. 4.7. With water, hydrogen sulphide, and aqueous ammonia, ditropyl ether (**27**), ditropyl sulphide (**28**), and ditropyl amine (**29**) were formed respectively, while with ethereal ammonia tritropylamine (**30**) was formed. Succinimide gave N-tropyl succinimide (**31**), and organometallic reagents gave the 7-substituted cycloheptatrienes (e.g., **32**–**34**). The cation is readily reduced by zinc to give bitropyl (**35**), and oxidized by chromic acid or silver oxide to benzaldehyde (**36**). The cation **5** can also react as an alkylating agent, and aromatic substitution occurs with phenols and tropolone. Thus, treatment of a mixture of phenol (**37**) and

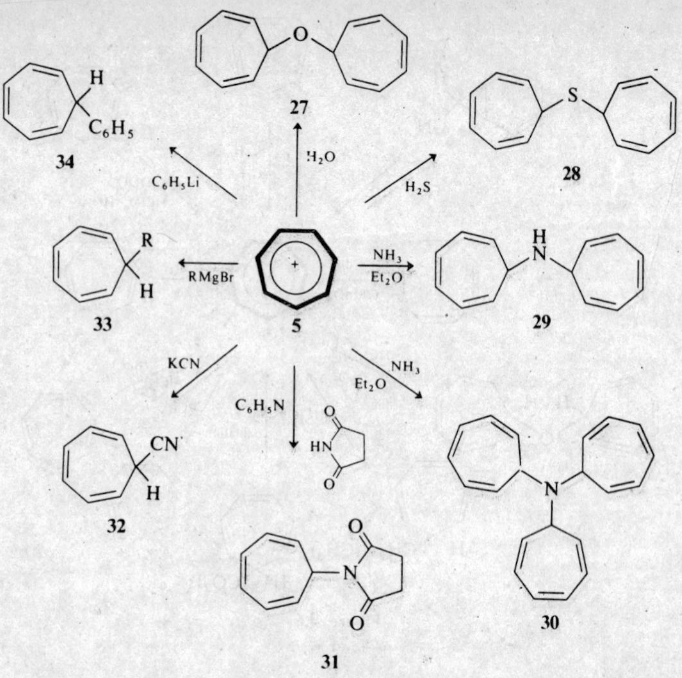

Figure 4.7

ditropyl ether (**27**) with HCl in ether gave 2-cycloheptatrienylphenol (**38**), while treatment of tropolone (**8**) with tropylium bromide (**5**) gave a mixture

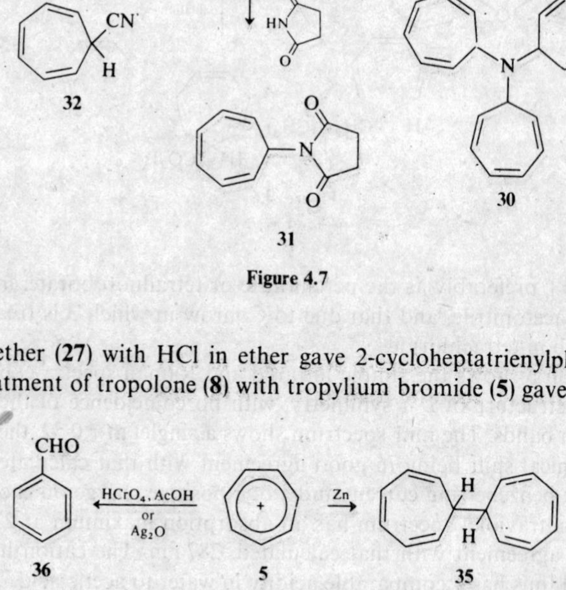

of **39**, **40**, and **41**. The compounds **39–41** are thermally labile, and isomerize by 1,5-hydrogen shifts to give compounds with other arrangements of the double bonds in the cycloheptatrienyl rings.

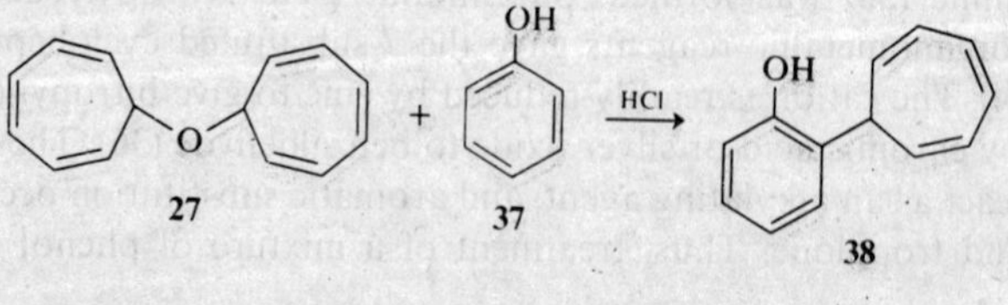

76

The cation **5** can, under appropriate conditions, form sandwich compounds of the ferrocene type. Thus treatment of cycloheptatrienyl molybdenum tricarbonyl (**42a**) with tritylfluoroborate in methylene chloride gave the tropylium complex **43a**, and the chromium complex **43b** can be prepared

42a	M = Mo	**43a**	M = Mo
42b	M = Cr	**43b**	M = Cr

in an analogous manner. The true 'sandwich' complexes of chromium and manganese (**45a, b**) were prepared by acylation of the corresponding complexes of benzene and the cyclopentadienyl anion (**44a, b**). The ring expansion presumably occurs because of the decreased tendency of the σ-transition state cation to aromatize when complexed to the metal.

In the case of the iron complexes, it appears that the tropylium cation acts as a four π-electron and not a six π-electron donor. Thus treatment of

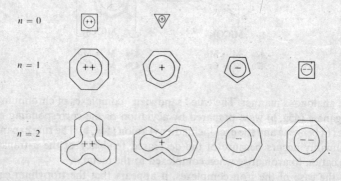

44a M = Cr
44b M = Mn

45a M = Cr
45b M = Mn

the iron tricarbonyl complex of cycloheptatrienyl methylether (**46**) with hydrofluoroboric acid gave the complex **47**. The structure **47**, in which the iron is complexed to two of the double bonds, with a ' free ' allylic cation, was obtained by X-ray crystallographic and nmr studies. The structure is mobile, each of the double bonds in turn participating in bonding to the iron.

46

47a

47b

Numerous substituted and annelated tropylium cations have been prepared, and the physical and chemical properties investigated, but these will not be considered here. The synthesis of the tropylium cation led to a search for other charged systems which could potentially be aromatic, and the simpler cyclic ions which contain $(4n + 2)$ π-electrons are shown in Fig. 4.8.

The triphenylcyclopropenium cation (**51**), the first 2-π electron aromatic ion to be prepared, was synthesized by Breslow in 1957. Diphenylacetylene

$n = 0$

$n = 1$

$n = 2$

Figure 4.8 Potentially aromatic monocyclic ions containing $(4n + 2)$ π-electrons.

(48) reacts with phenyldiazonitrile **(49)** to give 1,2,3-triphenylcyclopropenyl cyanide **(50)**, which, on treatment with boron trifluoride etherate containing water, gave the triphenylcyclopropenium cation **(51)**. The cation reacts with methanol to give 3-methoxy-1,2,3-triphenylcyclopropene **(52)**, and **52** on treatment with HBr regenerates **51** as the bromide.

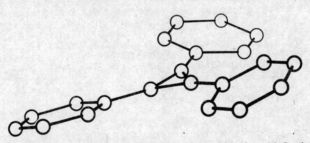

The nmr spectrum of the cation **51** shows that there is only one type of phenyl ring, while the ultraviolet spectrum is similar to that of **52**, except for a greatly increased intensity of absorption. An X-ray crystallographic analysis of **51** confirmed the symmetrical structure, and revealed that the phenyl rings are twisted 21° out of the plane of the cyclopropyl ring (Fig. 4.9).

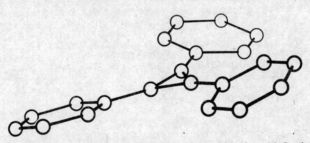

Figure 4.9   Structure of the triphenylcyclopropenium cation (data from M. Sundaralingham and L. H. Jensen, *J. Am. Chem. Soc.*, 1966, **88**, 198).

Simple HMO calculations predict a value of $2 \cdot 0\,\beta$ for the delocalization energy of the cyclopropenium cation **(53)**, and more extensive calculations suggested the cation should be stabilized by phenyl substituents, due to mesomeric interaction (Fig. 4.10). However, the subsequent synthesis of a number of alkyl substituted cyclopropenium cations (e.g., **54**) showed that not only were the phenyl substituents unnecessary, but that the alkylated ions were more stable than the arylated ions. This conclusion was reached from a study of the pK_{R^+} values of the ions, and the results are shown in Table 4.1. Nevertheless, a study of the ^{13}C nmr spectra of the cyclopropenium and tetraphenylcyclopropenium ions suggests that a considerable delocalization of charge occurs onto the benzene rings in the latter species.

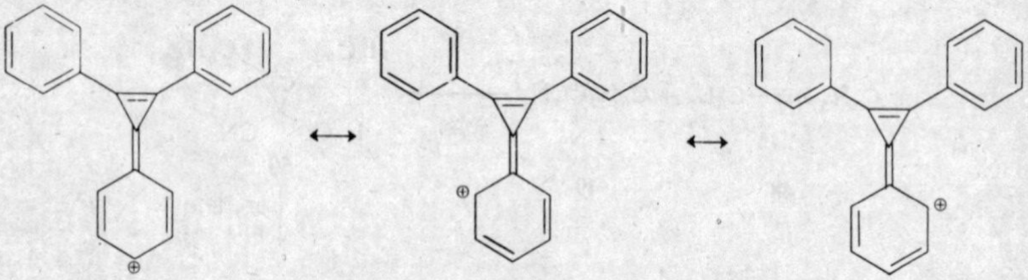

Figure 4.10

Quite recently the parent cyclopropenium cation (53) has itself been prepared. Reduction of tetrachlorocyclopropene (55) with tri-n-butyl tin hydride gave a mixture of mono and dichlorocyclopropenes, from which 3-chlorocyclopropene (56) was isolated. The nmr spectrum of 56 in SO_2 at $-40°$ shows only one type of proton, and it appears that in SO_2 ionization

Table 4.1

	pK_{R^+}
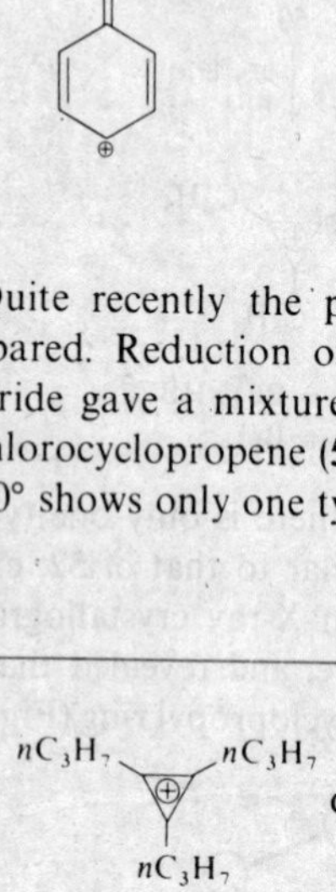 nC_3H_7 — nC_3H_7, nC_3H_7, $ClO_4^{\ominus}$	7·2
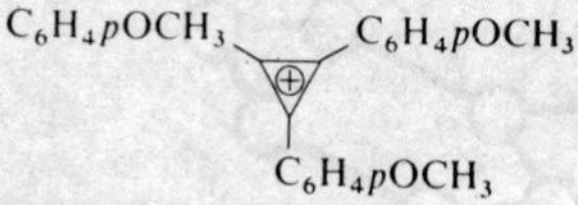 $C_6H_4pOCH_3$ — $C_6H_4pOCH_3$, $C_6H_4pOCH_3$, $Br^{\ominus}$	6·5
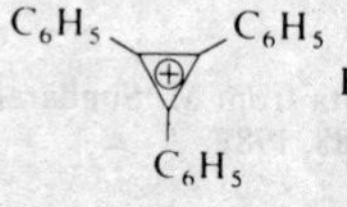 C_6H_5 — C_6H_5, C_6H_5, $Br^{\ominus}$	3·1
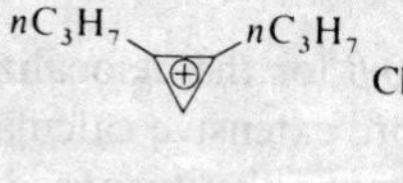 nC_3H_7 — nC_3H_7, $ClO_4^{\ominus}$	2·7
 C_6H_5 — C_6H_5, $Br^{\ominus}$	−0·67

Data from R. Breslow, H. Höver, and H. W. Chan, *J. Am. Chem. Soc.*, 1962, **84**, 3168.

occurs and the chlorine migrates rapidly around the ring. When **56** is treated with antimony pentachloride in methylene chloride, a white precipitate is formed, which was shown to be cyclopropenium hexachloroantimonate (**53a**). The salt **53a** is stable at room temperature in the absence of moisture,

but it is rapidly decomposed by water. The infrared spectrum is simple, showing only four bands as expected for a molecule with D_{3h} symmetry, and the nmr spectrum shows only one resonance signal at $\tau -1 \cdot 1$. The ^{13}C nmr resonance signal is in the expected position for the delocalized cation, and

the ^{13}C—H coupling constant, 265 Hz, suggests that the C—H bond has considerable s character. An orbital model of the cation can be formulated in which each carbon atom has an sp^2 orbital to the hydrogen, two sp^2 orbitals for the bent cyclopropenyl C—C bonds, and a p orbital contributing to the π-system (Fig. 4.11). A pK_{R^+} of $-7 \cdot 4$ has been observed for the cation, showing that it is much less stable than the substituted cyclopropenium cations (Table 4.1). However, this $pK_{R\oplus}$ still indicates that the cyclopropenyl cation is considerably thermodynamically more stable (*ca* 18 kcal.mole^{-1}) than the corresponding allyl cation.

The corresponding tetrafluoroborate **53b** and tetrachloroaluminate **53c** salts have been prepared, but these are stable only in solution. Evidence for the preparation of the cation **53** in solution has also been obtained when the pyrolysate from thermal decomposition of **57** is treated with fluorosulphonic acid. Presumably **58** is produced, together with diethyl phthalate **59**, and **58** subsequently decarboxylates under the influence of the strong acid.

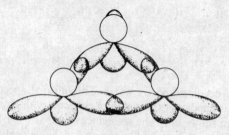

Figure 4.11 The bonding atomic orbitals in the cyclopropenium cation (the phases of the p_π atomic orbitals are distinguished by shading).

The cyclobutadienium dication (**60**), a second possible 2 π-electron system, has not been prepared, but two substituted dications **61** and **62** have recently been obtained. Initial attempts to prepare these dications gave only the

monocations **63** and **64**, although a subsequent investigation in which 3,4-dibromotetraphenylcyclobutene (**66**) was treated with silver tetrafluoroborate may have yielded the dication **62**. Firm evidence for the preparation of the cations **61** and **62** was advanced by Olah and his co-workers, who treated the dichloride **65** and the dibromide **66** with the extremely strong acid systems, SbF_5 and $FSO_3H\text{-}SbF_5$. The main evidence for the dication

structures came from ^{13}C magnetic resonance measurements. The chemical shift of the ^{13}C signal was shown to be 80 ppm below that of benzene for **61**, and 48 ppm below that of benzene for **62**. The difference in $\delta^{13}C$ for the two species was attributed to a delocalization of the charge onto the phenyl rings. A considerable degree of 1,3-interaction has also been suggested to occur in **62**, canonical forms such as **62b** making a significant contribution to the structure of the ion.

65 → SbF₅/SO₂ → **61**

66 → SbF₅/SO₂ → **62a** ↔ **62b**

Two further potential 6 π-electron systems are the cyclobutadienyl dianion (**67**), and the cyclooctatetraenyl dication (**68**). Attempts to prepare both of these systems have been reported but these have so far been unsuccessful.

67   **68**

It is in the 10 π-electron systems that the greater propensity for charged systems to attain a planar delocalized state as compared to the isoelectronic neutral systems is most clearly illustrated. Both the cyclooctatetraenyl dianion (**71**) and the cyclononatetraenyl anion (**76**) have been prepared, the latter in two different configurations, as planar, delocalized, aromatic systems. [10]Annulene, on the other hand, is a fugitive compound which appears to possess little or no aromatic character in any of its configurational forms (see chapter 3).

The cyclooctatetraenyl dianion (**71**) can be prepared by treatment of solutions of cyclooctatetraene (**69**) in ether, tetrahydrofuran or liquid ammonia with alkali metals. This reaction was originally reported by Reppe and his co-workers in their classical paper on the synthesis of cyclooctatetraene, and these investigators showed that a dialkali metal salt was formed, since carboxylation gave a dicarboxylic acid. Quenching the solution of the salt with water gave a mixture of cyclooctatrienes. A number of authors suggested that the dianion might have some aromatic character, but the first firm experimental evidence for this suggestion was provided by Katz in 1960, who studied the reaction of cyclooctatetraene with alkali metals by esr and nmr spectroscopy. Reduction of cyclooctatetraene occurs by two one-electron processes, to give first the radical anion **70**, and then the dianion **71**. The hyperfine structure of the esr spectrum showed nine lines

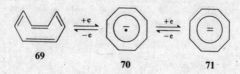

in the appropriate binomial ratio for eight equivalent protons, and the hyperfine splittings were consistent with a structure of D_{8h} symmetry. The nmr spectrum showed a single resonance at $\tau 4.3$, and the infrared spectrum was also simple. The chemical shift of the nmr signal is almost identical with that of cyclooctatetraene, and indicates that the shielding effect of the $\frac{1}{4}$ excess electron density on each carbon atom just balances the deshielding effect of the ring current. The calculated chemical shift of the cyclononatetraenyl anion based on the value for **71** is in excellent agreement with that found (see later, and chapter 2).

The addition of the first electron to cyclooctatetraene leads to the formation of the radical anion **70** having a planar conformation. The pseudo Jahn–Teller distortion which would occur in cyclooctatetraene (see chapter 2) is removed by the addition of an electron, giving an electronic non-degenerate state. The addition of the second electron fills the non-bonding orbital and gives a closed shell configuration (Fig. 4.12). Unlike the other ions previously

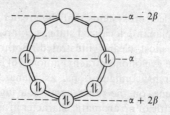

Figure 4.12

considered, the cyclooctatetraenyl dianion, in the simple HMO picture, does not gain in resonance energy on the addition of the electrons. The adoption of a planar configuration for the anion radical and dianion can be attributed to the removal of the degenerate electronic state which may occur in planar cyclooctatetraene, and to the delocalization of charge which can occur in the planar form. It appears that the main barrier to the reduction occurs in the addition of the first electron, in which the ring must flatten. Early studies suggested that this radical anion **70** rapidly disproportionated to give cyclooctatetraene and the dianion **71**, but this disproportionation has been shown to be strongly dependent on the nature of the counter-ion and solvent employed.

The ready availability of the dianion **71** has led to the extensive investigation of its chemistry. The dianion can act as both a reducing agent and as a nucleophile. Thus tropylium bromide **5** is reduced by **71** to ditropyl (**72**), while **71** is alkylated by methyl iodide to give the dimethylcyclooctatrienes **73** and **74**. The trienes **73** and **74** are thermally labile, and rearrange readily to other products.

The dianion **71** reacts with aldehydes, ketones, and acid chlorides as a nucleophile to give a variety of products. With *gem*-dihalides the dianion gives *cis*-bicyclo[6.1.0]nonatrienes (**75**) a reaction that is preparatively useful (Fig. 4.13). The dianion **71** has recently been shown to form ' sandwich ' complexes with uranium and thorium. An X-ray crystallographic analysis of the uranium compound has shown it to be of D_{8h} symmetry with planar, eclipsed C_8H_8 rings (Fig. 4.14).

The physical and chemical properties of the cyclooctatetraenyl dianion support the view that **71** is a planar, 10 π-electron, aromatic system.

The cyclononatetraenyl anion, the next higher homologue of the cyclopentadienyl anion, has been synthesized both in the thermodynamically stable, all-*cis* form **76** and also in the mono-*trans* form **81**. The mono-*trans* anion **81** is stable only below $-10°$ and rearranges to the all-*cis* anion **76** on warming.

The all-*cis* anion **76** can be prepared by treatment of 9-chlorobicyclo-[6.1.0]nonatriene (**77**) with lithium, by treatment of 9-methoxybicyclo-[6.1.0]nonatriene (**78**) with potassium, and by deprotonation of bicyclo-[6.1.0]nonatriene (**79**) or cyclononatetraene (**80**) with base (Fig. 4.15). The

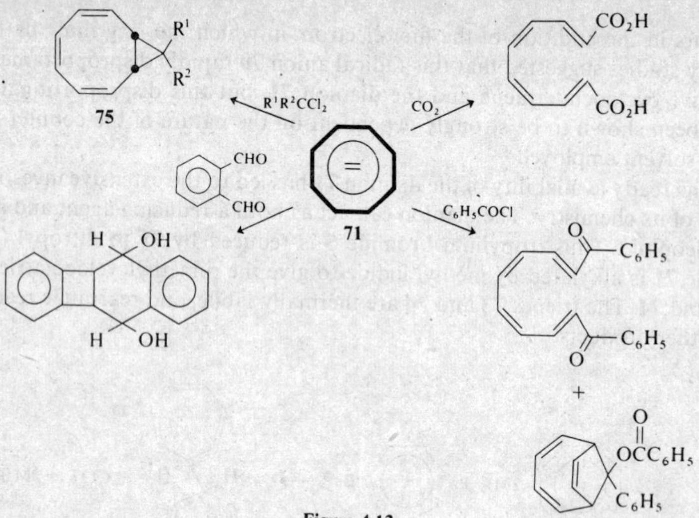

Figure 4.13

75

$R^1R^2CCl_2$ ← **71** → CO_2

CHO / CHO

H OH / H OH

CO_2H / CO_2H

C_6H_5COCl

O C_6H_5 / O C_6H_5

+

O $\overset{\|}{C}C_6H_5$ / C_6H_5

Figure 4.13

Figure 4.14

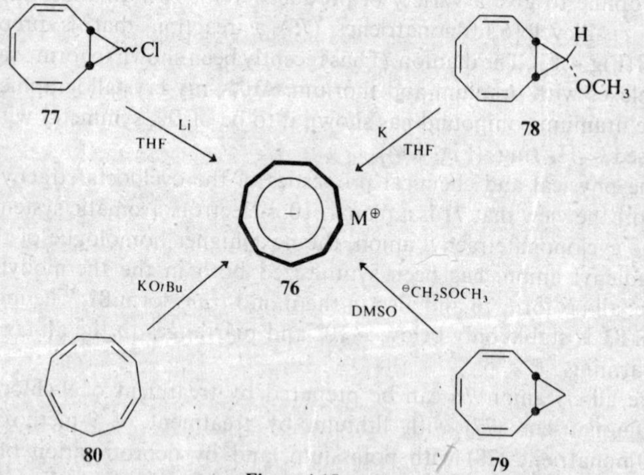

77 Cl

$\xrightarrow[\text{THF}]{\text{Li}}$

78 H OCH_3

$\xrightarrow[\text{THF}]{\text{K}}$

76 $M^{\oplus}$

$\xrightarrow{\text{KOtBu}}$

80

$\xleftarrow[\text{DMSO}]{^{\ominus}CH_2SOCH_3}$

79

Figure 4.15

86

formation of the all *cis*-anion **76** from *anti*-9-methoxybicyclo[6.1.0]non-atriene (**78**) with potassium, presumably via the cyclopropyl anion, is a process which is symmetry forbidden if concerted, since conrotatory ring opening of the cyclopropyl anion is predicted, and the mono-*trans* anion **81** should result. This led to an investigation of this reaction at $-40°$, when it was demonstrated that the *mono*-trans anion **81** is, in fact, initially formed (Fig. 4.16).

Figure 4.16

The anion **76**, which can be prepared as a crystalline tetramethylammonium salt, shows only one resonance signal in the nmr spectrum, at *ca* τ 3·0, depending on the nature of the counter-ion and the solvent. The position of absorption is in good agreement with that calculated from the position of the proton signal in the cyclooctatetraenyl anion (**71**), assuming that both systems have the same diamagnetic ring current. The ultraviolet spectrum of **76** is simple, showing a strong absorption at 251 nm, and a double, weaker maxima at *ca* 320 nm, and a calculated spectrum for a planar, D_{9h} structure is in accord with that found experimentally. The simple infrared spectrum is also that expected for a molecule of D_{9h} symmetry.

Equilibrium studies with cyclopentadiene and indene indicate that **76** is thermodynamically more stable than the cyclopentadienyl anion (**2**), and that cyclononatetraene must have a pK_a between 16 and 21 on the Streitweiser scale. The anion **76** reacts with water to give *cis*-cyclononatetraene (**80**) which is readily thermally rearranged to 8,9-dihydroindene (**82**). Hydrogenation of **76** over Pt/C gives a mixture of products, of which cyclononane (**83**) is the major component. Carboxylation gives 1-carboxy-8,9-dihydroindene (**84**), and methylation with methyl iodide gives 1-methyl-8,9-dihydroindene (**85**). The anion **76** reacts with N,N,N′,N′-tetramethylchloroformamidinium chloride (**86**) to give the nonafulvene **87**. These reactions are illustrated in Fig. 4.17.

The physical and chemical properties of the *cis*-cyclononatetraenyl anion (**76**) are those expected for a planar, 10 π-electron aromatic system.

The mono-*trans* anion **81** is stable at $-40°$, and the nmr shows the characteristic aromatic spectrum as found in the higher annulenes. The outer protons are low field (τ 2·73–3·6) and the inner proton appears as a triplet at very high field (τ 13·52). On warming to room temperature the anion was rapidly converted to the all *cis*-configuration, presumably by a similar process to that observed in the annulenes (see chapter 3).

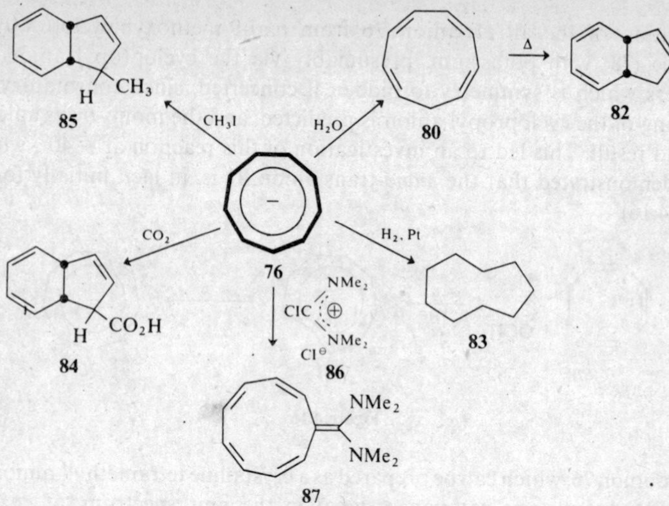

Figure 4.17

The bridged 1,6-methanocyclononatetraenyl anion (89) has also been prepared by proton abstraction from the triene 88. The outer protons resonate at low field while the inner methylene protons are at high field ($ca\ \tau\ 10·5$) in the nmr spectrum, and this anion thus also appears to have a delocalized, aromatic structure.

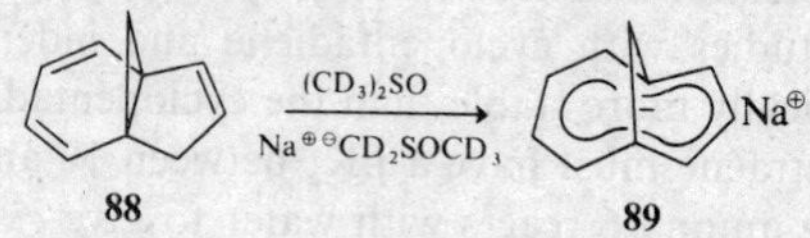

It has been shown that if the diamagnetic ring current is assumed to be constant in the series of ions $C_3H_3^{\oplus}$, $C_5H_5^{\ominus}$, $C_7H_7^{\oplus}$, then a plot of charge density at each carbon atom against the chemical shift from benzene is approximately a straight line (Fig. 4.18). However, when the 10 π-electron anions $C_8H_8^{\ominus}$ and $C_9H_9^{\ominus}$ are included, these deviate from the straight line, showing smaller shielding effects than expected. From these results it might appear that the induced diamagnetic ring currents in the 10 π-electron systems are greater than those in the 2 or 6 π-systems. This may, however, not be correct, since a plot of the ^{13}C chemical shift against the charge, again taking benzene as standard, is approximately linear for all of these ions, and it appears likely that the ^{13}C data is more reliable as a measure of charge density (Fig. 4.19).

The larger monocyclic anions and cations are, at present, poorly represented, but current research efforts in this area will probably soon alter

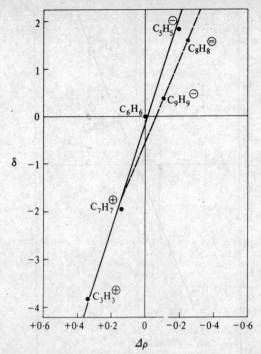

Figure 4.18 Charge density per carbon atom plotted against proton chemical shift in p.p.m. from benzene (from Garratt and Sargent, *Nonbenzenoid Aromatics*, ed. Snyder, Academic Press, 1971).

this position. The undecapentaenium cation (**90**) is unknown, but the corresponding bridged ion **92** has been prepared. Hydride abstraction from the tetraene **91** with tritylfluoroborate gives **92**, the nmr spectrum indicating that **92** is a delocalized, aromatic system. The outer protons resonate at low field while the proton on the methylene bridge appears as an AX system at high field (τ 10·3, 11·8) with a 10 Hz coupling. The electronic spectrum is similar to that of the benzotropylium cation, and **92** is thermodynamically more stable than the tropylium cation. In both **89** and **91** the methylene bridge removes the nonbonded interactions which would occur in the corresponding di-*trans* ions.

[12]Annulene (**93**), which is extremely unstable, can be reduced polarographically or by alkali metal reduction to give the [12]annulenyl dianion

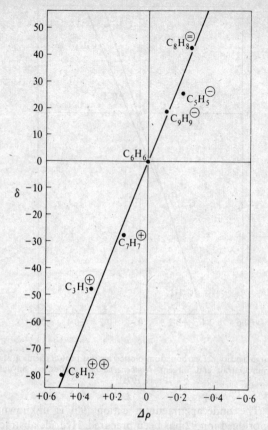

Figure 4.19 Charge density per carbon atom plotted against ^{13}C chemical shift, in p.p.m. from benzene (from Garratt and Sargent, *Nonbenzenoid Aromatics*, ed. Snyder, Academic Press, 1971).

(94). The reduction occurs by two one-electron additions, and the dianion 94 shows in the nmr spectrum three signals at τ 3·02, 3·77 and 14·6. The high field signal is due to the inner protons, and 94 thus exhibits a diamagnetic ring current. The spectrum is unaltered on warming to $+30°$, clearly indicating that the 14 π-electron dianion is much more stable than [12]annulene

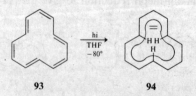

93   94

itself. The temperature independence of the nmr spectrum of **94** also reveals that there is no interconversion of inner and outer protons, a finding again different to that for **93**, in which such interconversion rapidly occurs.

Both bisdehydro[12]annulene (**95**) and tridehydro[12]annulene (**98**) are reduced by potassium, first to the corresponding radical anions (**96, 99**) and then to the dianions (**97, 100**) (Fig. 4.20). The radical anion **99** has the expected seven line esr hyperfine spectrum for a molecule with six equivalent protons, and the value of a_H (2·98 gauss) is similar, but slightly smaller, to the value found for the cyclooctatetraenyl radical anion. The nmr spectra of both the dianions **97** and **100** indicate that these molecules have a diamagnetic ring current, the inner proton H^3 appearing at τ 16·88. Reduction has converted the 12 π-electron neutral molecules, which have paramagnetic ring currents, into 14 π-electron systems, having diamagnetic ring currents.

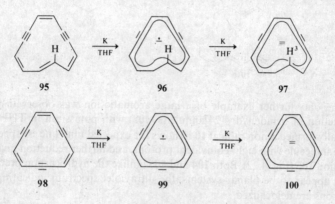

Figure 4.20

The higher homologue of the cyclooctatetraenyl dianion (**71**), the 18 π-electron [16]annulenyl dianion (**102**), has recently been prepared (Fig. 4.21). Reduction of [16]annulene (**101**) with a potassium-mirror in THF gave the dianion **102**, the nmr spectrum of which shows the twelve outer protons at low field, and the four inner protons at very high field (τ 18·17). The spectrum clearly indicates that **102** is a reasonably planar, delocalized aromatic compound, with a considerable induced diamagnetic ring current. The dianion **102** appears to exist in only one conformation, unlike [16]annulene itself, which, although predominantly **101a**, is in equilibrium with a small amount of **101b**. The nmr spectrum of **102** has been found to be invariant up to +140°, in striking contrast to the behaviour of the isoelectronic [18]annulene spectrum (chapter 3), and the delocalization energy of the dianion **102** must be *ca* 10 kcal.mole^{-1} greater than that of [18]annulene. A similar finding was made in the case of the dianion **97**, which is also conformationally rigid, unlike [14]annulene or its precursor **95**. These data once more emphasize the greater gain in resonance energy experienced by charged molecules, as compared to the corresponding neutral systems, on attaining a delocalized state.

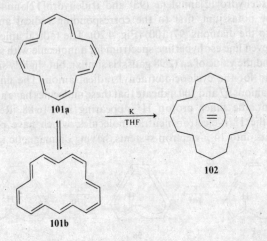

101a

$$\xrightarrow[\text{THF}]{\text{K}}$$

102

101b

The only further example of a large aromatic ion was observed in the reduction of octadehydro[24]annulene (103) with potassium in THF. The initially formed anion radical 104, shows the expected nine-line esr spectrum for a molecule with eight equivalent protons, and further reduction gives the dianion 105 (Fig. 4.22). Both 104 and 105, unlike the hydrocarbon precursor 103, appear to be planar systems, the ultraviolet spectrum indicating that the ions are delocalized.

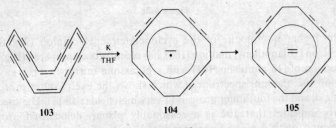

103   104   105

Figure 4.22

The examples of ions given in this chapter clearly indicate the value of the Hückel Rule in predicting the occurrence of aromatic systems. The smaller ions have been extensively investigated, and the only well authenticated examples of monocyclic, aromatic 10 π-electron systems are the cyclooctatetraenyl dianion (71), and the cyclononatetraenyl anions (76) and (81). There is at present considerably less known about the larger ionic systems, particularly in the case of the cations. However, the stability of the [12] and [16]annulenyl dianions, compared to the corresponding [14] and [18]annulenes, suggests that a number of these larger ions should be accessible. The possibility that bond alternation effects will not predominate until a larger ring size is reached than is the case with the neutral molecules is already suggested by the preparation of the anions **104** and **105**. Further experimental investigations in this area can be expected.

Further reading

For a general review of these systems, excluding the cyclopentadienyl anion and tropylium cation, see P. J. Garratt and M. V. Sargent, ' Monocyclic and Polycyclic Aromatic Ions Containing Six or More π-electrons ', in *Nonbenzenoid Aromatics*, Vol. 2, Ed. J. P. Snyder, Academic Press, 1971. Early work on the tropylium cation has been reviewed by T. Nozoe in *Progress in Organic Chemistry*, Ed. Cook and Carruthers, Volume **5**, 132, Butterworths, 1961.

Extensive reviews on the chemistry of ferrocene and related systems have appeared. See, for example, P. L. Pauson, *Organometallic Chemistry*, Arnold, 1967; D. E. Bablitz and K. L. Rinehardt, *Organic Reactions*, 1969, **17**, 1; G. Wilkinson and F. A. Cotton, *Progress in Organic Chemistry*, 1959, 1; M. Rosenblum, *Chemistry of the Iron Group Metallocenes*, Part 1, Wiley, New York, 1965.

For the reduction of [12]annulene, see J. F. M. Oth and G. Schröder, *J. Chem. Soc. B.*, 1971, 904; for the reduction of the dehydro[12]annulenes see P. J. Garratt, N. E. Rowland, and F. Sondheimer, *Tetrahedron*, **27**, 3157 (1971) and for the reduction of octadehydro[24]annulene see R. M. McQuilkin, P. J. Garratt, and F. Sondheimer, *J. Am. Chem. Soc.*, 1970, **92**, 6682.

5. Monocyclic antiaromatic ions

Besides the series of $(4n + 2)$ π-electron ions discussed in the preceding chapter, there is a corresponding series of ions with $4n$ π-electrons. The investigation of this series has only recently commenced, but already results of considerable interest have been obtained. In the HMO theory the $4n$ π-electron ions, like the neutral $4n$ annulenes, are predicted to have open, triplet ground state configurations. Thus the simplest member of the group, the cyclopropenyl anion (**1**) has three molecular orbitals, two of which form

1

a degenerate, antibonding pair. These are shown in Fig. 5.1. The simple HMO calculation, suggests that the cyclopropenyl anion will have no delocalization energy (DE=O) compared to a double bond and an isolated

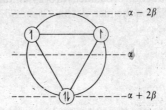

Figure 5.1

carbanion, and that it will be of *higher* energy than the correspondingly allyl anion, which has a DE of 0.83 β. Breslow has suggested the use of the term *antiaromatic* to describe conjugate, cyclic systems which are thermodynamically less stable than the corresponding acyclic analogues. Dewar has made a similar suggestion on the basis of perturbational m.o. calculations, which predict that planar cyclooctatetraene would be 2β *less* stable than octatetraene itself. Utilizing this definition a further classification of cyclic conjugated systems can be made. Such a system would then be *aromatic* if it has a larger

DE than its acyclic analogue, *nonaromatic* if it has the same DE as its acyclic analogue, and *antiaromatic* if it has less DE than its acyclic analogue.

This type of calculation again suffers from the difficulties in determining these energies. Either the heats of hydrogenation or combustion of real molecules can be found (e.g., cyclooctatetraene and octatetraene), or the DE of a non-real system (e.g., planar cyclooctatetraene) can be estimated by direct calculation or by the use of experimental data. Both of these methods are open to criticism of some kind. However, it seems likely that the term antiaromatic will be useful in describing molecules which are destabilized, rather than stabilized, by conjugation.

The concept of antiaromaticity is best illustrated in the case of ions, and in Fig. 5.2 a number of the smaller monocyclic $4n$ π-electron ions are shown.

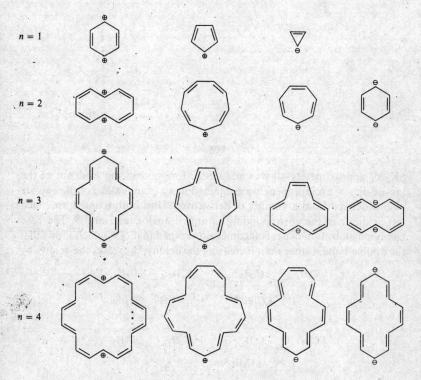

Figure 5.2 Potentially antiaromatic monocyclic ions containing $4n$ π-electrons.

The properties of a number of these ions, or related derivatives, are now known. The simplest system, the cyclopropenyl anion (**1**), is unknown, but Breslow and his co-workers have described a number of experiments in which attempts have been made to discover the properties of the triphenyl-cyclopropenyl anion (**2**) and related systems. Treatment of triphenylcyclo-propene (**3**) with sodamide in liquid ammonia gave hexaphenylbenzene (**5**) and not **2**. The reaction was shown to proceed through the intermediacy of the dimer **4**, and **2** is not involved (Fig. 5.3). Comparison with triphenyl-methane indicated that triphenylcyclopropene was much less acidic, and a

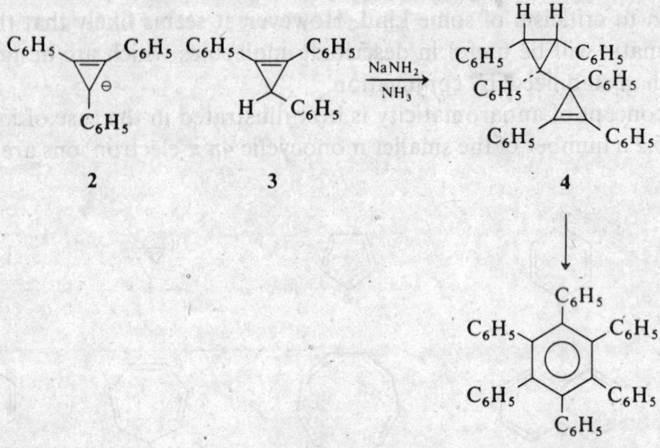

Figure 5.3

pK$_a$ of approximately 40 was adduced. More convincing evidence of the low acidity of cyclopropene was obtained in an examination of the enolate anions derived from a number of derivatives. Thus both **6** and **8** are much less acidic than the corresponding saturated analogues **7** and **9**. The base catalysed ionization of **8** is 6000 times slower than that of **9**, which shows that the double bond, rather than increasing the acidity, decreases the acidity by

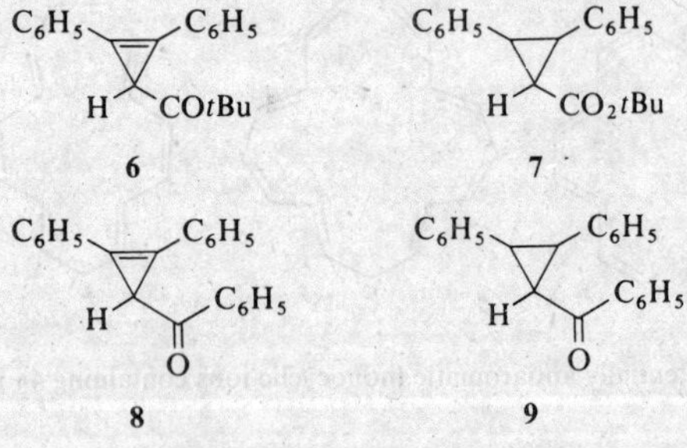

more than 7 pK units. This difference in acidity was largely attributed to the conjugative destabilization of the anion **10** by the antiaromaticity of the cyclopropenyl anion (Fig. 5.4).

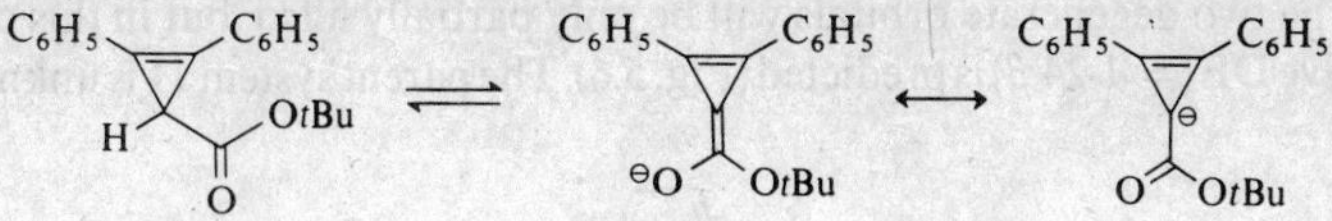

Figure 5.4

Recently a more direct estimate of the acidity of triphenylcyclopropene has been made using an electrochemical technique. For the thermodynamic cycle (i) shown in Fig. 5.5, the one-electron reductions of triphenylcyclopropene (ii) and triphenylmethane (iii) were examined. The formation of the alcohols from the hydrocarbons was taken to be independent of the nature of R, and E_1, E_1^1 and E_2, E_2^1 were determined by linear scan voltammetry.

(i) $RH \rightleftharpoons ROH \overset{K_1}{\rightleftharpoons} R^{\oplus} \overset{E_1}{\rightleftharpoons} R^{\odot} \overset{E_2}{\rightleftharpoons} R^{\ominus} \overset{K_2}{\rightleftharpoons} RH$

(ii) $(C_6H_5)_3CH \rightleftharpoons (C_6H_5)_3COH \overset{K_1}{\rightleftharpoons} (C_6H_5)_3C^{\oplus} \overset{E_1}{\rightleftharpoons} (C_6H_5)_3C^{\odot} \overset{E_2}{\rightleftharpoons} (C_6H_5)_3C^{\ominus} \overset{K_2}{\rightleftharpoons} (C_6H_5)_3CH$

(iii) $(C_6H_5)_3C_3H \rightleftharpoons (C_6H_5)_3C_3OH \overset{K_1^1}{\rightleftharpoons} (C_6H_5)_3C_3^{\oplus} \overset{E_1^1}{\rightleftharpoons} (C_6H_5)_3^{\odot} \overset{E_2^1}{\rightleftharpoons} (C_6H_5)_3C_3^{\ominus} \overset{K_2^1}{\rightleftharpoons} (C_6H_5)_3C_3H$

Figure 5.5

Knowing these values, then the difference in energy of these reactions $(E_1 + E_2) - (E_1^1 + E_2^1)$ can be determined. In this case

$$(E_1 + E_2) - (E_1^1 + E_2^1) = 1 \cdot 7 \text{ volts}$$

$$= 39 \text{ kcal.mole}^{-1} = 28 \text{ pK units at } 25° \quad (5.1)$$

Since pK_{R^+} of triphenylcyclopropenol is $+3\cdot1$ and that of triphenylmethane is $-6\cdot6$, then

$$\frac{K_1^1}{K_1} = 10^{9\cdot7} \quad (5.2)$$

and thus knowing from eq. (5.1) that the overall difference is 28 pK units then

$$\frac{K_2^1}{K_2} = 10^{18\cdot3}$$

Since triphenylmethane has a pK_a of 33, the triphenylcyclopropene must have a pK_a of *ca.* 51. This may be compared to the value of 58 for methane, and indicates that triphenylcyclopropene is an extremely weak hydrocarbon acid.

The cyclopentadienium cation (11), like the cyclopropenyl anion, is a $4n$ π-electron system with 4 π-electrons. Again the HMO calculation predicts that the two degenerate orbitals will be only partially filled, but in this case a positive DE ($= 1.24 \beta$) is predicted (Fig. 5.6). The parent system **11** is unknown,

11

but a number of derivatives have been prepared. Treatment of pentaphenyl-cyclopentadienol (**12**) with boron trifluoride in methylene chloride at $-60°$

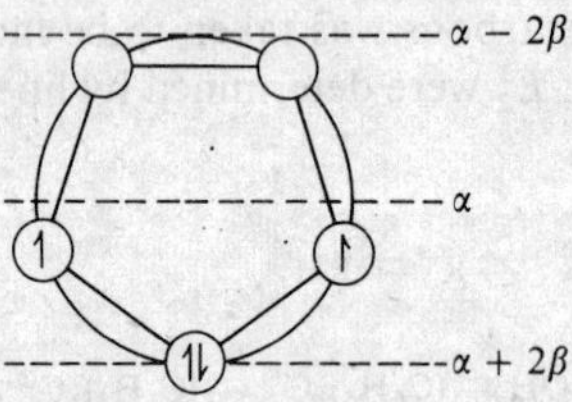

$$\alpha - 2\beta$$
$$\alpha$$
$$\alpha + 2\beta$$

Figure 5.6

gives a deep blue solution containing the cation **13**. This cation could exist either in the singlet **13a** or triplet **13b** states. The Jahn–Teller theorem suggests that the system should distort from the regular pentagonal structure, but the magnitude of this effect is not known.

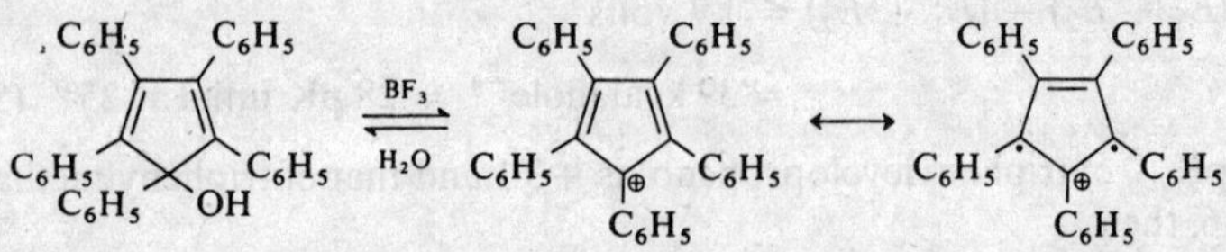

12   **13a**   **13b**

A frozen solution of the cation at 77K gave an esr spectrum characteristic of a triplet species. It was shown that the esr signal did not obey the Curie Law ($IT =$ constant, $I =$ intensity), and the slope obtained by the plot of signal intensity against temperature suggested that the triplet state lies about 1.3 kcal.mole^{-1} above the singlet ground state.

Since the triplet state should be favoured in smaller molecules, the penta-chlorocyclopentadienium cation (**15**) was prepared by treatment of hexa-chlorocyclopentadiene (**14**) with antimony pentafluoride. The esr spectrum again indicated the presence of a triplet species, and in this case the signal intensities obeyed the Curie Law. The pentachlorocyclopentadienium cation (**15**) thus has a triplet ground state **15b**. It thus appears likely that the parent cation **11** would also have a triplet ground state, indicating that the stabilization gained by the nondegenerate, unsymmetrical singlet state is small.

The 8 π-electron cycloheptatrienyl anion (**17**) was prepared by Dauben and Rifi in 1963. The HMO theory predicts that two electrons will occupy a pair of degenerate, antibonding orbitals, and that the anion will have a DE of $2 \cdot 10\beta$, considerably less than the tropylium cation ($2 \cdot 99\beta$). Semiempirical m.o. calculations suggest that the D_{7h} anion will be a triplet, but that the distorted singlet anion will be of lower energy.

Treatment of 7-methoxycycloheptatriene (**16**) with sodium-potassium alloy in THF at $-20°$ gave a deep blue solution of the cycloheptatrienyl anion (**17**), which could also be prepared by similar treatment of 7-triphenylmethylcycloheptatriene (**18**). Cycloheptatriene itself has been shown to undergo deuterium exchange under basic conditions, the cycloheptatrienyl anion (**17**) being the most probable intermediate.

The heptaphenylcycloheptatrienyl anion (**20**) was prepared by treatment of heptaphenyltropylium bromide (**19**) with potassium in ether. The blue solution of the ion **20** yields heptaphenylcycloheptatriene-7-d (**21**), and the solution shows an nmr spectrum and *no* esr triplet spectrum at low temperature. The heptaphenylcycloheptatrienyl anion thus appears to exist in the unsymmetrical singlet rather than the triplet ground state.

More recently some of the larger $4n$ π-electron systems have been prepared. A number of 15,16-dihydropyrenes react with alkali metals to give first the anion radical and then the corresponding dianions. Thus 15,16-dimethyl-dihydropyrene (**22**) gives first the radical-anion **23** and then the dianion **24** (Fig. 5.7). If **22** is considered to be a 14 π-electron system in which the central ethane bridge is a minor perturbation, then from HMO theory the added electron in the 16 π-electron dianion **24** would enter a degenerate pair of antibonding orbitals. However, the HMO theory is not likely to be reliable for these molecules, and the fact that **24** exists in a singlet state, showing a well-resolved nmr spectrum, is not unexpected. The nmr spectrum of **24** shows the expected *reversal* of proton chemical shifts for a molecule possessing a paramagnetic ring current. Thus the methyl protons on the inside of the ring now appear at very low field at $\tau -11.0$ compared to the high field position in **22** (τ 14.25), whereas the outer protons appear at high field at τ 13.2–14.0, instead of at low field as in the hydrocarbon **22** (τ 1.33–2.05). The paramagnetic effect observed in **24** is, from a comparison of the comparable

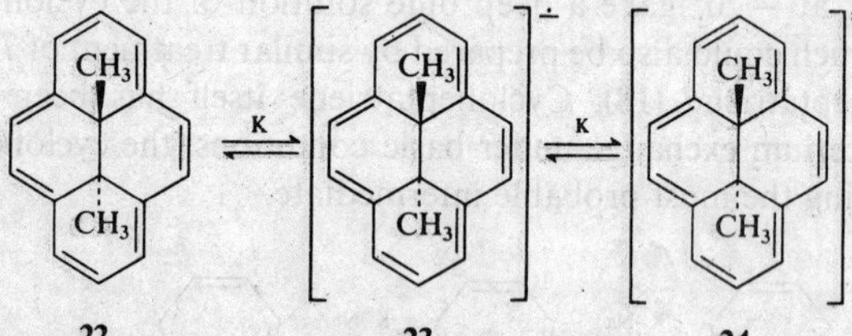

Figure 5.7

proton chemical shifts, greater than that observed in [16]annulene. This suggests a greater degree of mixing of excited states in **24**, which may be due to the increased rigidity of the system.

[18]Annulene (**25**) is reduced by potassium in THF also by two one-electron processes to give the anion radical **26** and the dianion **27** (Fig. 5.8). The dianion **27**, with 20 π-electrons, again shows the expected *reversal* of chemical shifts for the outer and inner protons as compared to **25**. Thus in the nmr spectrum of **27** at $-110°$ the inner protons appear as two broad singlets at $\tau -18.1$ and -19.5, and the outer protons as a broad singlet at τ 11.13. The appearance of two sets of inner protons is probably due to the occurrence of the dianion **27** in two conformations, **27a** and **27b**, whereas [18]annulene exists as only one conformational isomer. It may be remembered that in chapter 4 it was shown that [16]annulene, which exists in two interconverting configurations, gives the dianion in only one conformation. In both cases it seems that the energy difference between the conformations is *less* for the $4n$ π-electron systems.

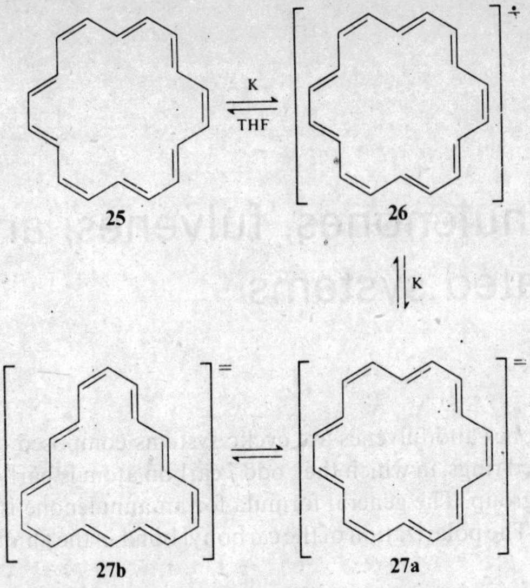

Figure 5.8

It appears from the $4n$ π-electron ions which have so far been prepared that only in the small ions is it likely that the triplet electronic configuration will be more stable than an unsymmetrical singlet ground state. Whereas in the smaller systems it should be possible to determine if the ions are destabilized by conjugation, in the larger molecules it will probably be difficult to find suitable model systems. The success in preparing the bridged 16 π-electron dianion **24** and the 20 π-electron dianion **27** may be indicative of stabilization in $4n$ π-electron molecules which exhibit paramagnetic ring current effects.

Further reading

For a review of some of the work described in this chapter, see *Advances in Organic Chemistry*, Volume **6**, p. 1.

For recent work on the cyclopropenyl anion, see R. Breslow and W. Chu, *J. Am. Chem. Soc.*, 1970, **92**, 2165, and references therein.

For the anions of the 15,16-dialkyldihydropyrenes, see R. H. Mitchell, C. E. Klopfenstein, and V. Boekelheide, *J. Am. Chem. Soc.*, 1969, **91**, 4931.

6. Annulenones, fulvenes, and related systems

The annulenones and fulvenes are cyclic systems composed of unsaturated, odd-membered rings, in which the ' odd ' carbon atom is part of an exocyclic unsaturated group. The general formula for an annulenone is **1**, and that of a fulvene is **2**. The polarization of the carbonyl bond in the annulenones leaves

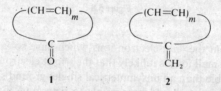

the ' odd ' carbon atom with a partial positive charge, and thus the annulenones with odd numbers of endocyclic double bonds are potentially aromatic, and those with even numbers of double bonds are potentially antiaromatic. However, for these effects to be manifest, the contribution of the polarized structure to the ground state must be important.

The simplest system which can attain aromaticity by this form of cross conjugation is cyclopropenone (**3**), which may be considered to be a

derivative of the 2 π-electron cyclopropenium cation. Substituted cyclopropenones have been known for some time and cyclopropenone (**3**) itself has recently been prepared, albeit only in solution, and it is much more stable than the saturated analogue, cyclopropanone (**4**). The synthetic scheme for the preparation of **3** is outlined in Fig. 6.1. The reduction of tetrachlorocyclopropene (**5**) with tri-*n*-butyl tin hydride gave a mixture of

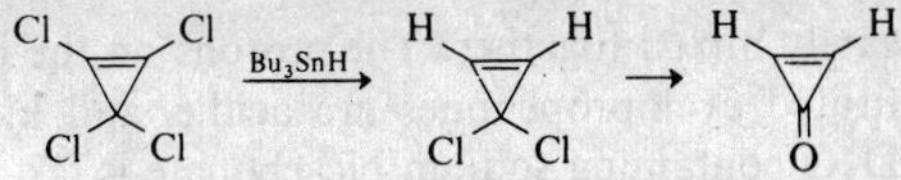

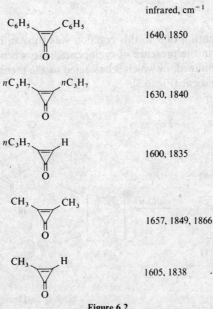

Figure 6.1

chlorocyclopropenes containing 3,3-dichlorocyclopropene (**6**), which is hydrolysed with cold water to cyclopropenone (**3**). The nmr spectrum of **3** shows a single absorption signal at τ 1·0, and there is a large ^{13}C proton coupling constant characteristic of a cyclopropene or an acetylene, the proton chemical shift position excluding the latter type system. The infrared spectrum shows a strong doublet at 1833 and 1864 cm^{-1}, again characteristic of cyclopropenones, and there is no absorption in the O—H region. Cyclopropenone is very soluble in water, but even in this medium it appears to be in the form of the ketone and not that of the hydrated *gem*-diol. Although the parent cyclopropenone can only be studied in solution, a number of substituted cyclopropenones have been prepared as relatively stable compounds, and some of these are shown in Fig. 6.2. All of these systems show two characteristic infrared bands in the region 1800–1870 and 1600–1660 cm^{-1}. These bands are due to the carbonyl and double bond stretching modes,

infrared, cm^{-1}

1640, 1850

1630, 1840

1600, 1835

1657, 1849, 1866

1605, 1838

Figure 6.2

but these are heavily mixed together. The protons on the double bonds of the mono-substituted cyclopropenones are acidic, and kinetic deuterium exchange with D_2O containing sodium bicarbonate is fast. Thus 2-propyl-cyclopropenone (7) exchanges the ring proton, under these conditions, presumably via the anion 8.

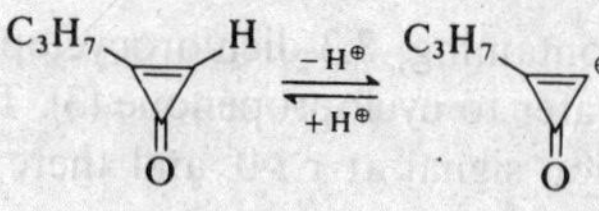

Cyclopentadienone (9) exists only in the form of its dimer, dicyclopenta-dienone (10), all attempts to prepare 9 yielding 10. Thus treatment of 4-bromo-cyclopentenone (11) with triethylamine gave 10 in virtually quantitative

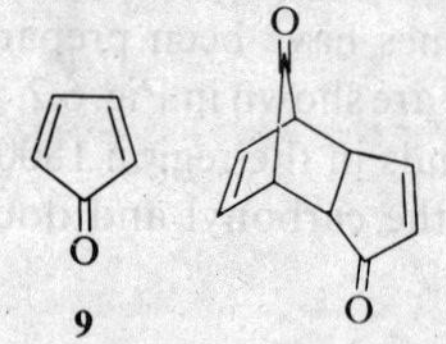

yield. The intervention of 9 in this reaction was substantiated by carrying out the reaction in the presence of cyclopentadiene, when the Diels–Alder adduct 12 was obtained, in which 9 has acted as the dienophile and cyclopentadiene as the diene (Fig. 6.3).

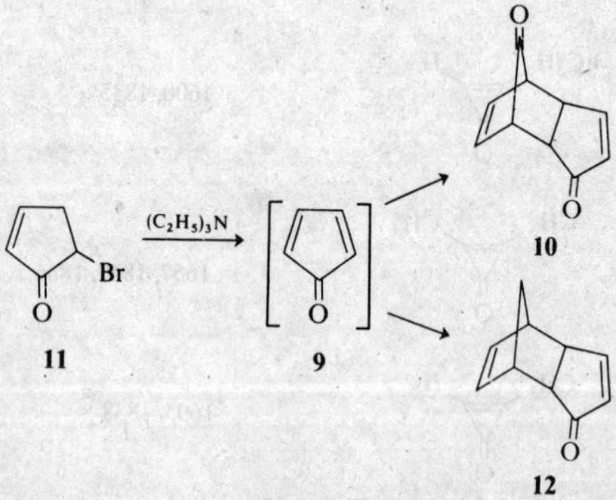

Figure 6.3

104

Attempts to reduce the reactivity of cyclopentadienone by ketalization again gave not the monomeric ketals but the corresponding dimers. When the diethyl ketal **14** was generated by treatment of the dibromoacetal **13** with potassium *t*-butoxide in the presence of maleic anhydride (**15**), the Diels–Alder adduct **16** was obtained, which was hydrolysed to the 7-norbornenone derivative **17** (Fig. 6.4).

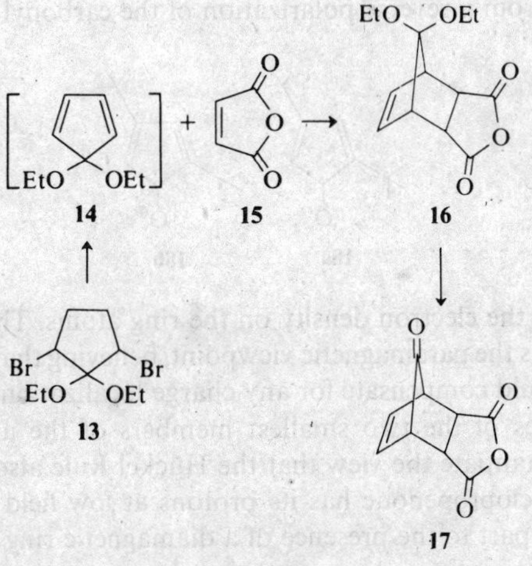

Figure 6.4

A number of sterically hindered cyclopentadienones have been prepared by Garbisch and Sprecher. 2,4-Di-*t*-butylcyclopentadienone (**18**) is a relatively stable compound that only dimerizes slowly at 25°. The Diels–Alder reaction between **18** and cyclopentadiene occurs more rapidly at 25° to give a mixture of products in which **18** has acted both as a diene and a dienophile. 3-*t*-Butylcyclopentadienone (**19**) is much more reactive than **18**, and with cyclopentadiene it gives only the adduct **20**, in which **19** has acted as the dienophile.

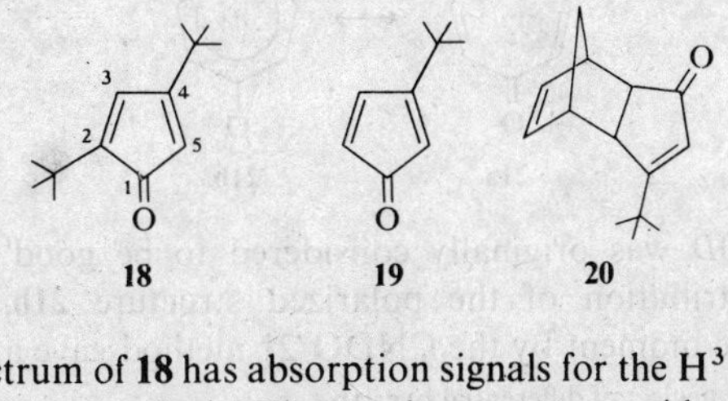

The nmr spectrum of **18** has absorption signals for the H^3 and H^5 protons at τ 3·50 and 5·07 respectively. These values are at considerably higher field than those expected for the α and β protons of an unsaturated ketone, and two explanations can be advanced. The high field position of these protons would be expected if the cyclopentadienone acted as a 4 π-electron system, with the consequent paramagnetic ring current effect of a 4n annulene. The 4 π-electron nature of **18** would arise from the contribution of the polarized structure **18a**. Garbisch and Sprecher rejected this view on the grounds that the t-butyl protons resonate in a normal position and do not show any upfield shift. They considered that the upfield shift of the ring protons arises from a reverse polarization of the carbonyl group, as in **18b**,

18a   **18b**

which increases the electron density on the ring atoms. The present author is biased towards the paramagnetic viewpoint, believing that the diamagnetic effect in **18b** would compensate for any charge localization.

The properties of the two smallest members of the annulenone series appears to substantiate the view that the Hückel Rule also applies to these compounds. Cyclopropenone has its protons at low field in the nmr, presumably due in part to the presence of a diamagnetic ring current, whereas the substituted cyclopentadienones have the proton resonances at high field. The high reactivity of cyclopentadienone may be seen as a reflection of the antiaromaticity of the contributing polarized structure, involving the cyclopentadienium cation.

Tropone, **21**, was one of the earliest molecules to be synthesized as a test of the predictions of the Hückel theory. It is a stable compound, in contrast to cyclopentadienone, and for many years after its synthesis was generally accepted to be an aromatic system. However, the basis for this assumption has recently been questioned, and it has been concluded from a study of its physical properties that tropone is not an aromatic system. The dipole

21a   **21b**

moment of 4·30D was originally considered to be good evidence for a substantial contribution of the polarized structure **21b**. However, the calculated dipole moment by the CNDO/2† method gave a value of 3·88D.

† CNDO – complete neglect of differential overlap.

Similarly, the use of more recent values for the Pascal constants gave a value for the diamagnetic anisotropy of -47.4, which is close to the experimental value of -54. Calculations with cyclopropenone indicate that this system does exhibit a diamagnetic ring current effect, and calculations on cyclopentadienone indicate that this molecule is less polarized than either cyclopropenone or tropone, but that the differences between the $4n$ and $(4n + 2)\pi$-electron systems is small. It thus appears likely that these molecules in which cross-conjugation is required for delocalization to occur will not show pronounced aromatic properties.

The fulvenes are systems related to the annulenones, the exocyclic carbonyl group having been replaced by an exocyclic methylene group. The simplest member of the series, methylenecyclopropene (22) has not been synthesized, but a number of derivatives of this system have been prepared. A Wittig

22

reaction between diphenylcyclopropenone (23) and the ylid 24 gave the methylenecyclopropane derivative 25 as a yellow crystalline solid. In the nmr spectrum of 25, the methylene proton appears at τ 4.98, which is at considerably higher field than the corresponding proton (τ 3.2) in the methylenecyclopropane 26. This upfield shift may be attributed to the shielding effect in the dipolar contributor 25b.

Reaction of malonitrile with diphenyl (23a) or di-n-propylcyclopropenone (23b) in the presence of base gives the corresponding methylenecyclopropenes 27a, 27b. Whereas the aryl substituted methylene cyclopropenes have electronic spectra with absorption maxima above 350 nm, the di-n-propyl derivative 27b shows only an absorption at 246 nm (log ε 4.3), indicating that the phenyl groups make an important contribution to the long wavelength absorption.

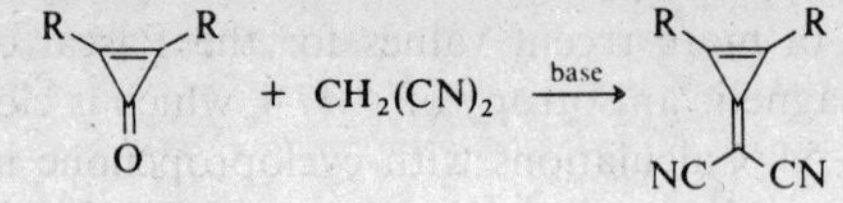

$$\underset{\substack{\text{23a} \quad R = C_6H_5 \\ \text{23b} \quad R = nC_3H_7}}{\text{R} \diagdown \diagup \text{R}} + CH_2(CN)_2 \xrightarrow{\text{base}} \underset{\substack{\text{27a} \quad R = C_6H_5 \\ \text{27b} \quad R = nC_3H_7}}{\underset{\text{NC} \quad \text{CN}}{\text{R} \diagdown \diagup \text{R}}}$$

The first methylenecyclopropene to be prepared was the orange quinonoid derivative **28** obtained by Kende. This molecule can be considered to be either a methylenecyclopropene or a vinylogous cyclopropenone.

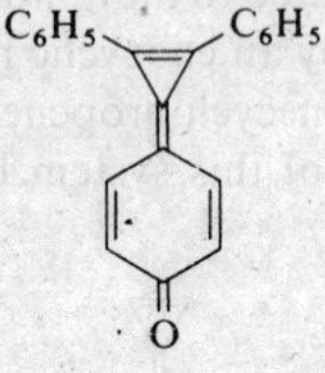

28

Fulvene, **29**, after which this series of molecules is named, is a much less reactive compound than cyclopentadienone, and it can be isolated and distilled as the monomer. Substitution at the exocyclic methylene position gives the 6-substituted fulvenes, which are still more stable. The exocyclic double bond is polarized, the exocyclic carbon atom being electron deficient with respect to the endocyclic carbon atom. Addition of metal alkyls occurs

29

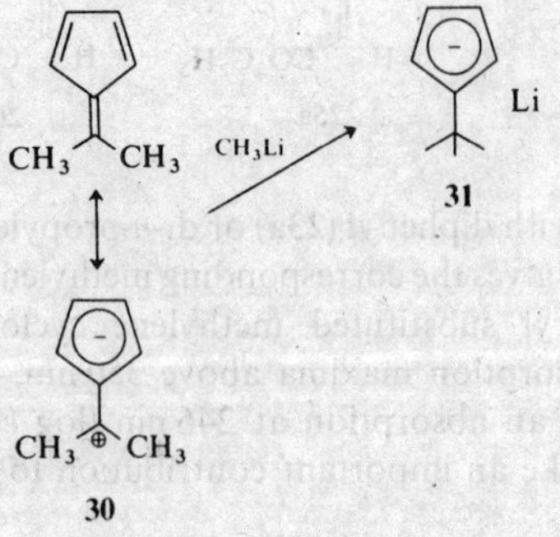

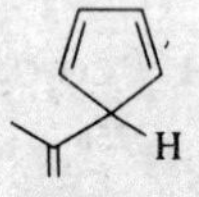

across the exocyclic double bond to give the substituted cyclopentadienyl anion (e.g., **30 → 31**). The stabilization of the cyclopentadienyl anion makes the methyl hydrogens in **30** acidic, and 6,6-dimethyl fulvene in many reactions behaves as the tautomeric structure **32**. The fulvenes are reduced with alkali metals first to the radical anion, which either dimerizes or is reduced further to the dianion.

6,6-Dimethylfulvene (**30**) reacts with maleic anhydride to give the Diels–Alder adducts **33a** and **33b**. By contrast, 6,6-(dimethylamino)fulvene (**34**), with electron withdrawing substituents at C-6, does not give Diels–Alder adducts with dienophiles. On reaction with tetracyanoethylene, the substitution product **35**, and not the Diels–Alder adduct, is obtained.

Heptafulvene (**39**) was prepared by von Doering and Wiley in 1954 by the reaction sequence shown in Fig. 6.5. Methyl diazoacetate adds to benzene to give 7-cycloheptatrienyl carboxylate (**36**), which was converted to the amine **37** via the corresponding amide. Exhaustive methylation of **37** gave the trimethylammonium iodide **38**, which on treatment with silver oxide underwent a Hofmann elimination to give deep red solutions of **39**.

Heptafulvene is only stable in dilute solution, polymerization occurring on increasing the concentration. It is stable to base treatment, but is rapidly polymerized by acids, probably via the formation of the methyl tropylium cation, which initiates polymerization. The electron spectrum is best accommodated by assuming that **39** is planar, with localized single and double bonds. Simple HMO theory predicts a high DE for **39**, which it undoubtedly does not possess.

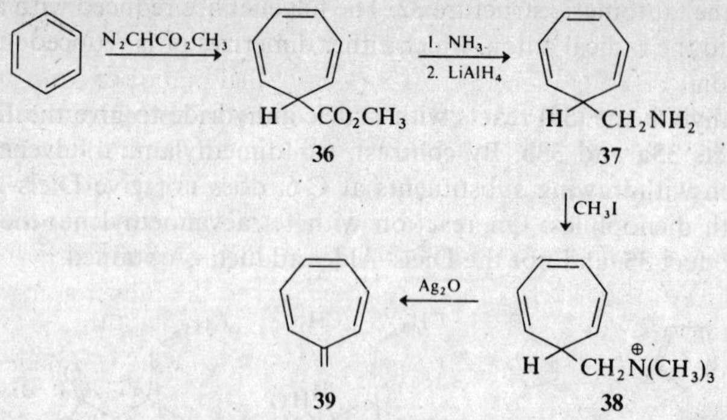

Figure 6.5

Heptafulvene reacts with dimethyl acetylenedicarboxylate (40) to give the Diels–Alder adduct 41, involving an orbital symmetry allowed 8 + 2 cyclo-addition (Fig. 6.6)

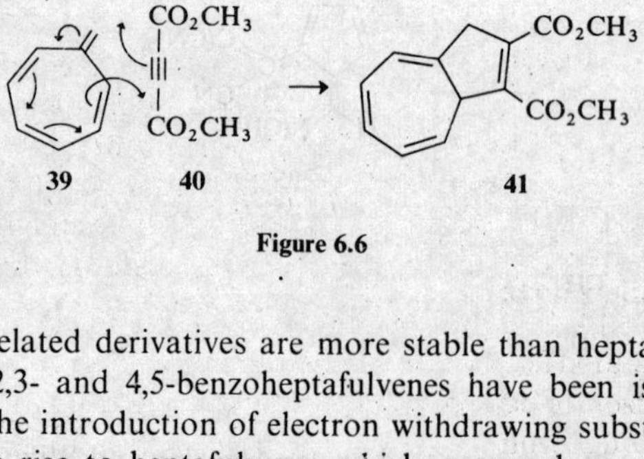

Figure 6.6

The benzannelated derivatives are more stable than heptafulvene itself, and both the 2,3- and 4,5-benzoheptafulvenes have been isolated as air sensitive oils. The introduction of electron withdrawing substituents in the 8-position gives rise to heptafulvenes which are much more stable than either the parent or benzannelated compounds. The increased stability is due to the increased importance of the dipolar form, involving the tropylium cation. Thus 8,8-dicyanoheptafulvene (42a) is a stable compound, having a large dipole moment (7·49D), both arising from a significant contribution of the dipolar structures 42b, 42c.

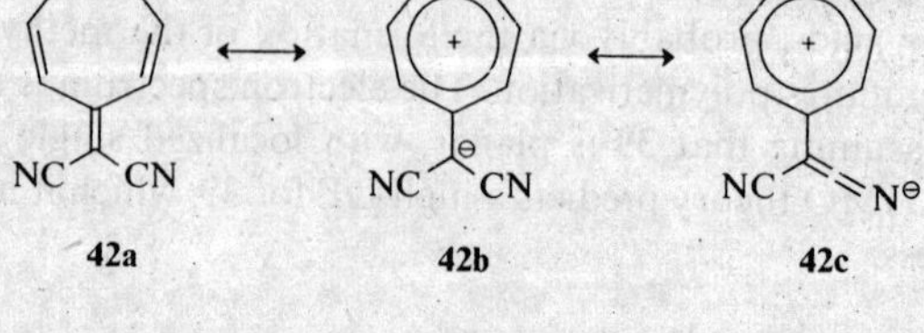

The properties of methylenecyclopropene, fulvene, and heptafulvene do not suggest that there is much alternation of structural type between the compounds with odd and those with even numbers of double bonds. Whereas cyclopentadienone is readily dimerized and tropone is not, fulvene is more stable than heptafulvene. Although 8,8-dicyanoheptafulvene appears to be stabilized by the contribution of dipolar structures, there is very little evidence which would encourage the term aromatic to be applied to the fulvenes as a group.

The fulvalenes are a group of molecules related to the fulvenes, in which the protons on the exocyclic fulvene double bond are replaced by a second 'odd' unsaturated ring, giving the general formula 43. The fulvalenes can

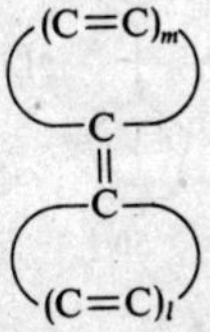

43

44

be further classified into those compounds in which m and l are both odd or both even integers, and those in which m is odd and l is even. The simplest fulvalene, triafulvalene (44) is of the first type ($m = l = 1$), and neither it nor any of its derivatives have so far been prepared. The next member of the series, triapentafulvalene (45a), belongs to the second type ($m = 1, l = 2$), and a number of derivatives of this system have been prepared. These compounds, which are also called calicenes, appear to be stabilized by a significant contribution from the dipolar form 45b. Thus hexaphenyltriapentafulvalene (46) has a dipole moment of 6·3D.

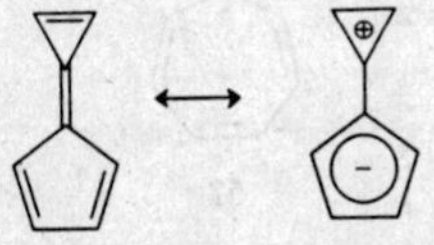

45a

45b

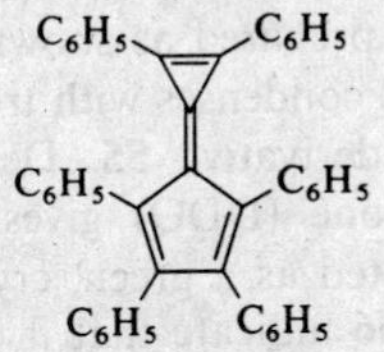

C_6H_5 C_6H_5

C_6H_5 C_6H_5

C_6H_5 C_6H_5

46

The next member of the series, fulvalene (**51**) itself, was prepared by von Doering and Matzner by the route shown in Fig. 6.7. Sodium cyclopentadienide (**48**) was oxidized with I_2 at $-80°$ to the dimer **49**, which on treatment with *n*-butyl lithium was deprotonated to give the dianion **50**. Oxidation of **50** in pentane with oxygen gives an orange solution of fulvalene (**51**). Attempts to concentrate this solution gave only polymeric products, but reaction with TCNE gave a Diels–Alder adduct, from which fulvalene could be regenerated. The ultraviolet spectrum of **51** is complex, showing maxima at 266, 278, 289, 300, and 314 nm. The intensity of the absorption increases

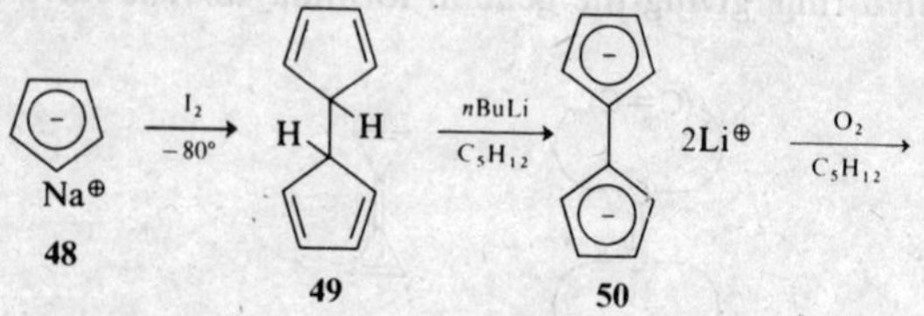

Figure 6.7

at longer wavelength, the 314 nm band having an extinction coefficient of 47,000. Fulvalene has also been prepared by oxidation of dihydrofulvalene with oxygen in the presence of silver oxide, and by photoirradiation of diazacyclopentadiene in a matrix at 77K. Numerous annelated and substituted fulvalenes have been prepared, and these can be isolated as stable, polyenic systems.

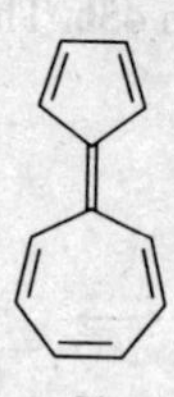

52

Sesquifulvalene, **52**, has only been obtained in solution, but it has been characterized by its chemical reactions and spectral properties. The tetraphenyl derivative **56** can be prepared as shown in Fig. 6.8. Sodium tetraphenylcyclopentadienide (**53**) condenses with tropylium bromide **54** to give the dihydrosesquifulvalene derivative **55**. Dehydrogenation of **55** with 2,3-dichloro-5,6-dicyanoquinone (DDQ) gives 7,8,9,10-tetraphenylsesquifulvalene (**56**), which is isolated as a green, crystalline solid. The physical and chemical properties of **56** indicate that it can be regarded principally as a polyene, with little contribution from **56b**. A number of other substituted

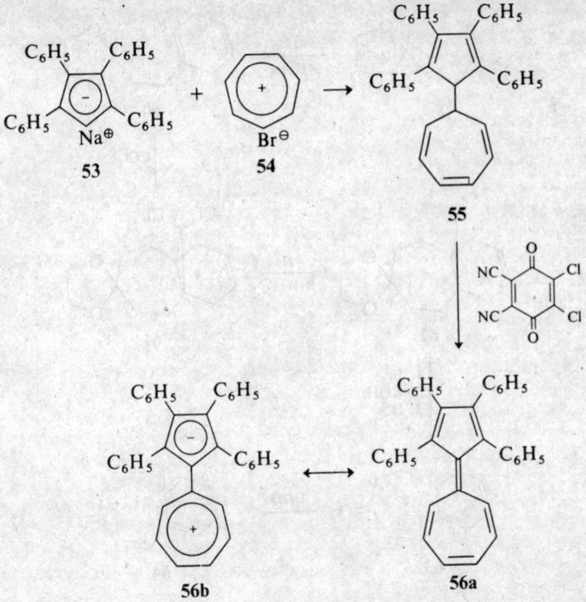

Figure 6.8

sesquifulvalenes have been prepared, and again the contribution of the dipolar structure to these molecules appears small. Both types of fulvalenes thus have similar properties, and, like the fulvenes, are best represented as polyenes rather than aromatic compounds.

A number of medium and macrocyclic annulenones, fulvenes and fulvalenes have recently been prepared. The nonafulvene **57** and the heptanonafulvalene **58** have been synthesized, and in both of these compounds the nine-membered ring is non-planar, the molecules behaving as polyenes.

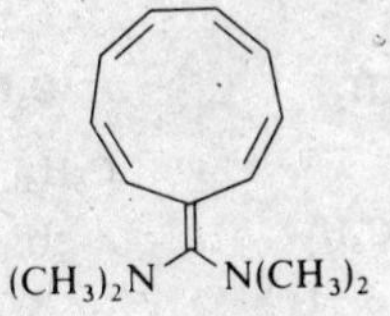

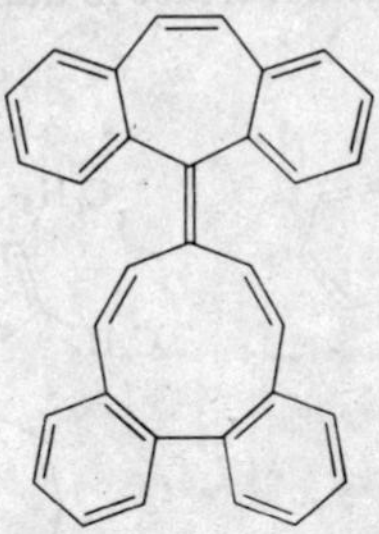

4,9-Methano[11]annulenone (**64**) was prepared by the route outlined in Fig. 6.9. The ketal **59** was reduced by lithium in liquid ammonia to the

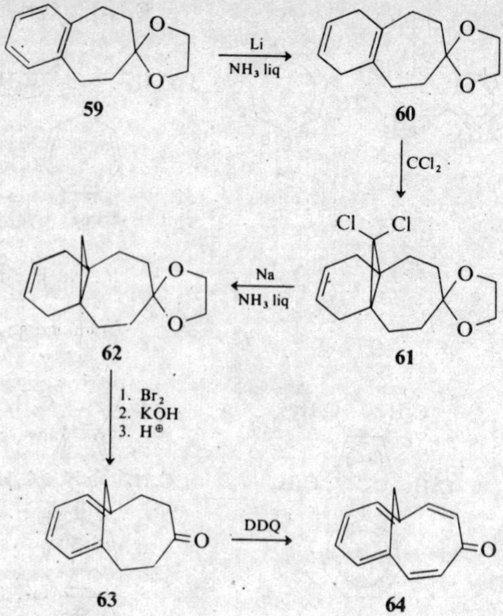

Figure 6.9

dihydro derivative **60**, which, on the addition of dichlorocarbene gave the tricyclic compound **61**. Dechlorination gave **62**, which on bromination, dehydrobromination gave the ketone **63**, which was dehydrogenated with DDQ to the annulenone **64**. The nmr spectrum shows the ring protons in the range τ 2·8–4·0, and the vicinal coupling constants have been interpreted in favour of a polyenic rather than an aromatic structure. Thus [11]annulenone, like tropone, appears to have little aromatic character. However, on protonation a considerable downfield shift of the ring protons occurs, indicating an increase in the diamagnetic ring current in the oxonium ion.

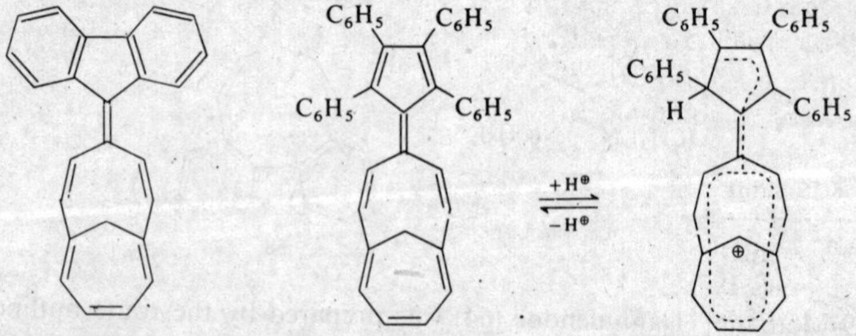

114

Two undecapentafulvenes **65**, **66** have been prepared by reaction of the 1,6-methanoundecapentaenium cation with either the fluorenyl anion or tetraphenylcyclopentadienide. In the nmr spectrum of both compounds the protons on the 11-membered ring are at relatively high field, and this observation, together with the vinylic coupling constants, again suggests that these are polyenic and not aromatic systems. However, protonation of **66** with trifluoroacetic acid gave the corresponding undecapentaenium cation **67**, the ring protons now appearing at much lower field in the nmr spectrum.

The macrocyclic dehydroannulenones containing 13, 15, and 17-membered rings have been prepared by the general synthetic method given in Fig. 6.10

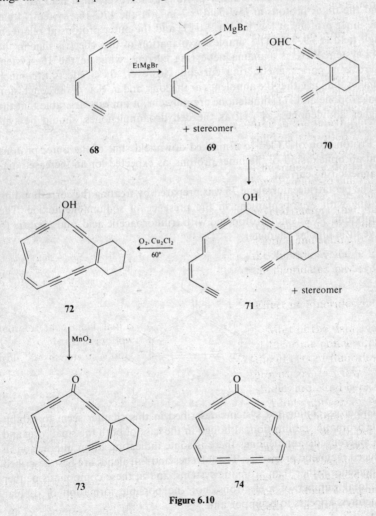

Figure 6.10

115

for the 15-membered ring compound. *cis,trans*-Octa-3,5-dien-1,7-diyne (**68**) was treated with a molar equivalent of ethylmagnesium bromide and the resulting Grignard reagent **69** (a mixture of 2 stereomers) was then treated with the aldehyde **70**. The resulting mixture of alcohols was oxidatively coupled under the Glaser conditions (only the stereomer **71** is in a suitable configuration to undergo this reaction) to give the cyclic alcohol **72**. Oxidation with manganese dioxide gave the [15]annulenone derivative **73**.

The ketones **73** and **74**, containing 15 and 17-membered rings show an interesting difference of chemical shifts in the nmr spectrum. Whereas the 15C-14π system **73** has the inner protons at relatively high field (*ca* τ 5·0) and the outer protons at low field (τ 2·35–3·7), the 17C-16π system **74** has the inner protons at low field (τ −0·31) and the outer protons at relatively high field (τ 3·9–5·0). The simplest explanation of this effect is that in the 14π-system there is a diamagnetic ring current, while in the 16π-system there is a paramagnetic ring current. However, these effects are much smaller than in either the annulenes or the ions, and in view of the conclusion that tropone and [11]annulenone are polyenic, it appears desirable that the higher annulenones, as well as the dehydroannulenones, should be synthesized.

Protonation of **73** led to a marked downfield shift of the outer protons and an upfield shift of the inner protons, as expected for an increased diamagnetic ring current.

The pentatridecafulvalene **75** was prepared by treating the corresponding ketone with cyclopentadiene in the presence of sodium methoxide. The compound **75** was not protonated with trifluoroacetic acid, and appears to have little dipolar character.

75

The cross conjugated systems described in this chapter seem to exhibit little aromatic stabilization, although in the case of both the small ring and the macrocyclic annulenones there is some indication of an alternation in induced magnetic properties. The fulvenes and fulvalenes are best described as polyenes rather than aromatic systems, and in these compounds neither the total number of π-electrons, nor the possible formation of dipolar structures, appears to be important.

Further reading

For a general discussion of these systems see *Advances in Organic Chemistry*, Volume **6**, p. 1.

For more recent reference to cyclopropenones see R. Breslow, G. Ryan, and J. T. Groves, *J. Am. Chem. Soc.*, 1970, **92**, 988.

For references to cyclopentadienone chemistry see E. W. Garbisch and R. F. Sprecher, *J. Am. Chem. Soc.*, 1969, **91**, 6785.

For a discussion of the aromaticity of tropone see D. J. Bertelli, T. G. Andrews, and P. O. Crews, *J. Am. Chem. Soc.*, 1969, **91**, 5286; D. J. Bertelli and T. G. Andrews, *J. Am. Chem. Soc.*, 1969, **91**, 5280.

The chemistry of fulvenes and related compounds has been reviewed by E. D. Bergmann, *Chem. Revs.*, 1968, **68**, 41.

For the larger annulenones and related systems see G. P. Cotterrell, G. H. Mitchell, F. Sondheimer, and G. M. Pilling, *J. Am. Chem. Soc.*, 1971, **93**, 259, and references therein.

7. Heterocyclic systems

7.1 Introduction

There are two types of heterocyclic systems which in principle could exhibit aromatic properties: type (i), in which the heteroatom replaces a carbon atom in a carbocyclic aromatic compound and provides one electron to the π-system and type (ii), in which the heteroatom replaces a carbon–carbon double bond unit (C=C) and provides two electrons to the π-system. Pyridine (**1**) is the classical example of type (i), and pyrrole (**2**) that of type (ii).

The properties of pyridine would be expected to be similar to those of benzene, the differences being due to the difference in electronegativity of nitrogen and carbon. Whereas benzene has D_{6h} symmetry, with all the carbon atoms and C—C bonds equivalent, pyridine is a distorted hexagon with C-2 equivalent to C-6, C-3 equivalent to C-5, and C-4 unique. In the simple HMO treatment, the σ framework of pyridine is considered to be hexagonal, the nitrogen atom is sp^2 hybridized, the lone pair of electrons occupying one of these orbitals. The remaining p orbital then combines with the carbon p atomic orbitals to form a set of six molecular orbitals (Fig. 7.1). The six π-electrons can then occupy three bonding molecular orbitals, as in benzene. Two problems now arise, how to account for the alteration in the regular hexagonal σ framework of benzene by the substitution of nitrogen, and how to estimate the values of the coulomb and resonance integrals for the C—N bond. One approach is to ignore the change in the σ framework and allow all of the changes to be absorbed in the coulomb and resonance integrals. Taking the empirical parameters α and β for the coulomb and resonance integrals of benzene, then these can be modified so that

$$\alpha_N = \alpha + h_N\beta \tag{7.1}$$

and

$$\beta_{CN} = k_{CN}\beta \tag{7.2}$$

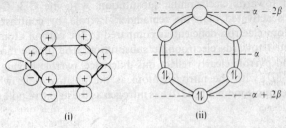

Figure 7.1 (i) p_π atomic orbitals of pyridine, (ii) molecular orbitals of pyridine, assuming $\alpha_N = \alpha, \beta_{CN} = \beta$.

The problem is then to assign specific values to the h_N and k_{CN} parameters for nitrogen. For elements, such as nitrogen, which are more electronegative than carbon the value of h will be positive, and α_N should be greater than α. However, the value of h presumably also depends on the number of electrons contributed by the heteroatom to the π-system, and should differ in pyridine and pyrrole. The value of k depends on the bond length. Streitwieser has given values for the h and k parameters for a number of heteroatoms, taking into account the number of electrons donated by the heteroatom and the bond order. The values of $h_N = 0.5$ and $k_{CN} = 1$ were suggested for nitrogen in pyridine. These values can now be introduced into eqs. (7.1) and (7.2), and the new values for α and β introduced into the appropriate place in the determinant (1.20).

A similar treatment can be applied to pyrrole (**2**). In this case the nitrogen p atomic orbital combines with the four carbon p orbitals to form five molecular orbitals similar to those of the cyclopentadienyl anion (Fig. 7.2). The values suggested for nitrogen in pyrrole are $h_N = 1.5$ and $k_{CN} = 1$, although calculations have been carried out using a relatively wide range of values for these parameters.

The general conclusions of the m.o. theory are perforce in general agreement with the earlier inductive ideas of the English school of chemists. Pyridine is thus found to be polarized so that the nitrogen has an excess of π-electron density, with the carbons electron deficient. Pyridine is generally

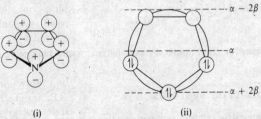

Figure 7.2 (i) p_π atomic orbitals of pyrrole, (ii) Molecular orbitals of pyrrole, assuming $\alpha_N = \alpha, \beta_{CN} = \beta$.

119

deactivated towards electrophilic substitution, with the C-3, C-5 atoms being less deactivated than the remainder. Pyrrole, by contrast, has the nitrogen atom electron deficient as compared to the carbon atoms, and is thus activated towards electrophilic substitution. The dipole moments of pyridine and pyrrole clearly reflect this difference, pyrrole having a dipole moment ($1 \cdot 8D$) with the nitrogen atom as the positive pole, whereas in pyridine the dipole moment ($2 \cdot 2D$) has nitrogen as the negative pole (Fig. 7.3).

$2 \cdot 2D$ $1 \cdot 8D$

Figure 7.3

The electronic spectrum of pyridine resembles that of benzene, three major absorption bands being observed. However, the long wavelength bands are more intense than those in benzene, since due to the lower symmetry of pyridine these transitions are no longer forbidden. The spectrum of pyrrole is less readily explained, and its similarity to that of cyclopentadiene has been interpreted both for and against the supposition that pyrrole is a delocalized system.

The nmr spectrum of pyridine clearly highlights the effect of introducing nitrogen for carbon. The H^2, H^6, and H^4 protons appear at lower field than those of benzene, and the H^3, H^5 protons at higher field, due to the changes in electron density (Fig. 7.4). In pyrrole, all of the protons attached to carbon are at higher field than those in benzene, again indicating the change in electrondensity, due in this case to electron donation by nitrogen. The nmr behaviour of these compounds is thus consistent with the direction of the dipole moment, and is also consistent with the reactivity towards electrophilic substitution.

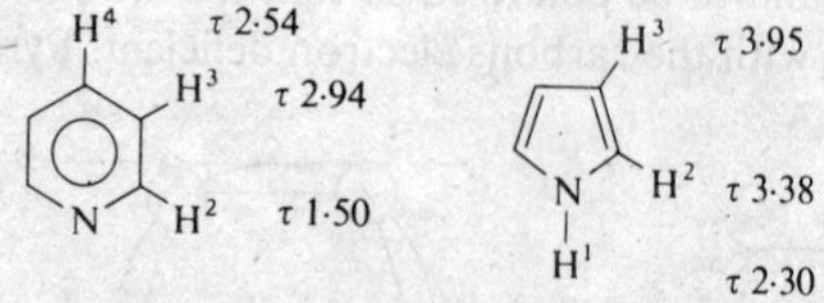

Figure 7.4   Nmr proton chemical shifts in pyridine and pyrrole.

7.2 Pyrrole type systems

Other electronegative elements besides nitrogen may be conceptually substituted for the methylene group in cyclopentadiene to form heterocyclic analogues of pyrrole. Further, the substitution of heteroatoms into other 'odd' cyclic systems, such as cyclopropene, will give a series of molecules of the general type **3**. Assuming a two-electron contribution from the heteroatom, then those systems in which m is odd will contain $4n$ π-electrons, and

$$\text{\Large(=)}_m^{\text{\Large(}}\!\!\!\big)$$
$$\underset{X}{}$$

3

those in which m is even will contain $4n + 2$ π-electrons. The first four members of this series are shown in Fig. 7.5.

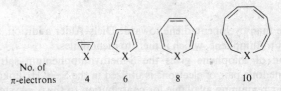

No. of				
π-electrons	4	6	8	10

Figure 7.5 Heterocyclic homologues of the pyrrole type.

The most usual heteroatoms to have been introduced are oxygen, nitrogen, and sulphur, although a number of 6 π-electron compounds containing silicon, germanium, and other elements have been prepared. The 3-membered ring compounds with $m = 1$ are $4n$ systems containing 4 π-electrons and as such should not be aromatic. Representatives of these systems have not so far been prepared. Early reports of the preparation of acetylene oxide (**4**) are now known to be incorrect. The matrix reaction between NH and acetylene at 52K did not give **5**, but may have given ketenimine. A number of azirines have been prepared, such as **6**, but these do not show any tendency to isomerize to derivatives of **5**.

$$\underset{4}{\overset{\triangle}{O}} \qquad \underset{\underset{H}{N}}{\overset{\triangle}{\underset{5}{}}} \qquad \underset{6}{\overset{\triangle}{N}}\!\!{-}C_6H_5$$

The compounds with $m = 2$ have 6 π-electrons and are aromatic. This group is made up of the familiar compounds pyrrole (**2**), furan (**7**), and thiophene (**8**). These molecules have very different properties from those of cyclopentadiene, being far less reactive than would be expected for a fixed, *cisoid* diene. In all of these systems the heteroatom forms the positive end of the dipole, in contrast to the saturated analogues, in which the heteroatoms are the negative end. Pyrrole is a very weak base, due to the lone pair of

121

electrons on nitrogen being involved in the delocalized π-system, which would be destroyed on protonation. In fact, pyrrole protonates in strongly acid media not on nitrogen but on carbon. The importance of the delocalized π-system is nicely demonstrated for thiophene, which on oxidation with perbenzoic acid gives the dimeric derivative **9**, rather than the sulphoxide. Thiophene dioxide, which has not been isolated, thus appears to be even

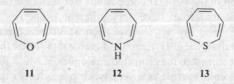

more reactive than cyclopentadiene towards Diels–Alder addition, in complete contrast to thiophene, which is inert to dienophiles.

Methylation of thiophene gives the S-methylthiophenium salt **10**, in which only one lone pair of electrons is utilized in the S—CH$_3$ linkage, the other lone pair remaining available for contribution to the 6 π-system.

All three heterocycles undergo electrophilic substitution, furan being the most reactive and thiophene the least. Due to the electron donation by the heteroatom, the carbons have excess electron density, and the compounds are more reactive than benzene. This is in complete contrast to pyridine, which is less active than benzene towards electrophiles. Furan reacts readily with dienophiles to give Diels–Alder adducts, whereas pyrrole normally gives substitution products and, as we have mentioned, thiophene does not react.

The heterocyclic systems with $m = 3$ contain 8 π-electrons, and are isoelectronic with the tropylium anion. These compounds should not then exhibit aromatic behaviour. Whereas the parent oxepin (**11**) is known, only derivatives of azepine (**12**) and thiepin (**13**) have been prepared. Vogel and his co-workers prepared oxepin by the route outlined in Fig. 7.6, which was subsequently modified to prepare 1,6-methano[10]annulene. Epoxidation of 1,4-cyclohexadiene gave the epoxide **14**, which on bromination gave **15**. Dehydrobromination of the dibromide **15** gave a tautomeric mixture of benzene

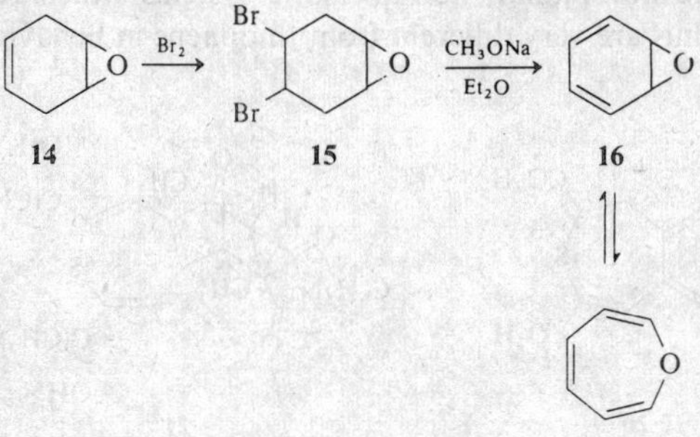

Figure 7.6

oxide (**16**) and oxepin (**11**). The nmr spectrum indicated that a *ca* 1:1 mixture of **16** and **11** was present, and the temperature dependence of the spectrum indicated that the interconversion between **16** and **11** is rapid. The oxepin molecule is non-planar, existing in a pseudo-tub conformation, and a rapid interconversion of the nonplanar conformations **11a** and **11b** also occurs. The electronic spectrum indicates that the equilibrium between **11** and **16**

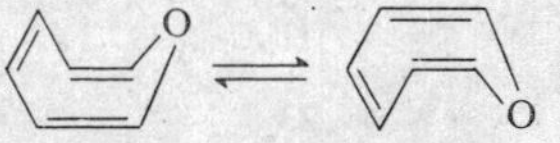

is extremely solvent dependent, the amount of **16** increasing in more polar solvents.

A number of N-substituted azepines have been prepared (e.g., **17, 18**) and these have all been shown to be non-planar, having pseudo-tub structures. Unlike oxepin, the azepines show little tendency to valence tautomerize to the corresponding bicyclic tautomers (e.g., **19**). The nmr spectrum of **17** is

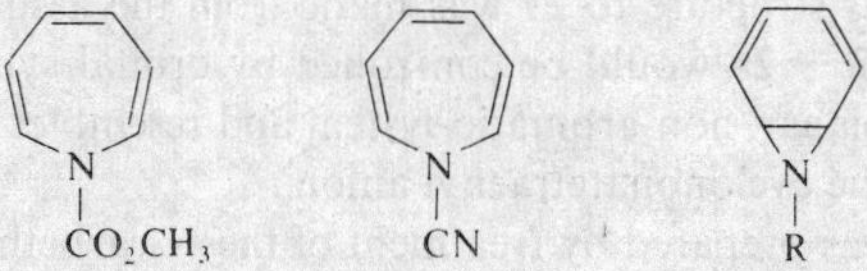

123

very similar to that of cycloheptatriene, and the ultraviolet spectrum shows a high intensity maximum at *ca* 210 nm, and two less intense bands at *ca* 240 and 330 nm. The azepines have the properties expected for polyenes.

The only simple thiepins are those which are benzannelated (e.g., **20**), although a complex alkylated thiepin **21** has recently been prepared. These compounds are non-planar, non-aromatic systems which readily extrude sulphur, and thus are very different from thiophene in behaviour.

20   21

The systems with $m = 4$ contain 10 π-electrons, are isoelectronic with the cyclononatetraenyl anion, and should be aromatic. Both the parent oxonin (**22**) and azonine (**23**) systems have been recently prepared, but only substituted derivatives of thionin (**24**) are known. Oxonin (**22**) was prepared

22   23   24

by the low temperature ($-80°$) photoirradiation of cyclooctatetraene epoxide (**25**). The nmr spectrum of oxonin has resonance signals in the region τ 3·79–4·92, and the spectrum is temperature independent. Oxonin is thermally unstable, rearranging to the *cis*-bicyclic compound **26** at 30°. Photoirradiation leads to the formation of an equilibrium mixture of **22** and an extremely labile compound that is probably mono-*trans* oxonin (**27**). This latter isomer rearranges below $-15°$ to the *trans*-bicyclic compound **28**. The assignment of the mono-*trans* structure to **27** was made from the assumption that the rearrangement **27** → **28** would be controlled by orbital symmetry. Oxonin is clearly a non-planar, non-aromatic system and resembles cyclononatetraene rather than the cyclononatetraenyl anion.

Azonine (**23**) was prepared by treatment of the N-carbethoxyazonine (**29**) with potassium tertiary butoxide in THF at low temperature. The nmr spectrum of **23** consists of a two-proton double doublet at τ 2·85, a four-proton multiplet at τ 3·27, and a broad two-proton multiplet at τ 3·92–4·25. Hydrogenation of **23** over rhodium on charcoal at 0° gave azacyclononane

(**30**). Azonine is thermally more stable than oxonin, and is recovered unchanged after warming to 50°. The chemical shifts of the protons in the nmr spectrum of **23**, at lower field than the corresponding protons in oxonin and the N-carbethoxy derivative **29**, together with the greater thermal stability was interpreted as indicating that azonine has some aromatic character. However, it is quite clear that these heterocyclic systems do not resemble the cyclononatetraenyl anion, but have mainly polyenic properties.

The annelated thionin **31a**, and the corresponding oxonin **31b** are also non-planar, non-aromatic compounds. Both are relatively stable crystalline

31a X = S
31b X = O

compounds, the annelation preventing the thermal ring closure exhibited by the unsubstituted heteronins.

At the present time only a few compounds are known which have heterocyclic rings containing more than nine atoms. All of these larger systems, such as **32**, contain a variety of substituents, and all appear to be non-planar, localized systems. It is to be expected that more extensive investigations

32

will be carried out with the object of preparing the parent systems. In general it appears that the smaller members of this series exhibit the alternation of properties observed in the annulenes and the monocyclic ions, but the delocalization energy gained is smaller and the stabilization of the planar state dies off more rapidly. The 9-membered ring heterocycles thus resemble polyenes rather than aromatic molecules, but since bond angle strain and non-bonded interactions are large in these compounds, an investigation of the larger unsubstituted homologues may more conclusively reveal the limit for delocalization in this type of system.

7.3 Pyridine type systems

Since oxygen is divalent rather than trivalent, it is not possible to replace the nitrogen in pyridine by oxygen to give a neutral system. However, treatment of 4-pyran (**33**) with triphenylmethyl perchlorate removes a hydride ion and leads to the formation of the corresponding pyrylium salt **34**. The pyrylium salts dissolve in water to give acidic solutions, which

$$(C_6H_5)_3C^{\oplus}ClO_4^{\ominus}$$

$$ClO_4^{\ominus}$$

33   34

contain an equilibrium mixture of the cation **34** and the pseudobase **35**. The pyrylium salts are more stable than the corresponding trialkyloxonium

126

$$\text{34} \quad X^{\ominus} + H_2O \rightleftharpoons \text{35} + HX$$

salts, but this increased stability is small. The cationic nature of these compounds tends to mask the aromatic properties, but these compounds do not appear to possess the aromatic stabilization found in pyridine.

4-Pyran (33) is an air-sensitive, unstable liquid, and its properties resemble those of a vinyl ether. 4-Pyrone (36), a compound that is isoelectronic with tropone, is a much more stable system. 4-Pyrone undergoes electrophilic substitution rather than addition, and is stable to acids, two properties unexpected for a vinylogous lactone. Ring opening does, however, occur readily under basic conditions, and the stability is not as great as was once thought. 2-Pyrone (37) has similar properties to 36, although it is more readily ring opened. The stability of the pyrones to acids arises from the formation of the corresponding pyrylium salts (e.g., 38).

Sulphur, like oxygen, is divalent, and the thiopyrylium salts, for example 39, are stable, delocalized systems. However, sulphur, unlike oxygen, has accessible d-orbitals which could become involved in bonding. Suld and Price demonstrated that such bonding could occur by treatment of the thiopyrylium salt 39 with phenyl lithium, when the S-phenylthiabenzene 40 was formed. This compound was fairly readily oxidized, but it could be isolated as a crystalline compound, m.p. 65°, and its infrared, ultraviolet, and nmr spectra were determined. The nmr spectrum shows only a single resonance at τ 2·66, indicating that the thiabenzene ring sustains a diamagnetic ring current similar to that in benzene. The dipole moment (1·88D) suggests that the molecule is not primarily in the polar ylid form (e.g., 40b).

127

The corresponding S-methylthiabenzene was also prepared, and this proved to be less stable than **40**. A number of thianaphthalenes have, however, been isolated and these are reasonably stable towards oxidation or thermal rearrangement and have aromatic type spectra.

The other elements in the nitrogen group can be trivalent, and can in principle be substituted for the nitrogen of pyridine to give a neutral hetero system. Although phosphabenzene or phosphorin, **41**, is itself unknown,† a

41

number of substituted phosphorins have been prepared. The first of these, 2,4,6-triphenylphosphorin (**44**), was prepared by Märkle by the reaction of the pyrylium salt **42** with the phosphine derivative **43**. 2,4,6-Triphenyl-phosphorin is a stable, crystalline compound, the nmr spectrum of which

shows a doublet signal at τ 1·9 for H^3, H^4 and a multiplet at τ 2·2–3·0 for the aromatic protons. The phosphorus nmr spectrum shows a large downfield shift compared to H_3PO_4 ($-178\cdot2$ Hz), the ultraviolet spectrum has a maximum at 278 nm (ε 41,000), and shows a large bathochromic shift when compared to 2,4,6-triphenylbenzene and 2,4,6-triphenylpyridine (both 254 nm). These spectral data clearly indicate that **44** is a delocalized system, and this was confirmed by an X-ray crystallographic study, which showed the phosphorin ring as a planar, distorted hexagon, with long C—P bonds (1·75°), and a small CPC angle (103°).

A variety of substituted phosphorins were subsequently prepared, including 2,4,6-tri-t-butylphosphorin, **45**, at present the one derivative having only

45

† See, however, further reading.

alkyl substituents. The phosphorins are readily reduced by alkali metals to give first the anion radical, then the dianion, and finally the trianion radical.

Phosphorus, like sulphur, also has d-orbitals available for bonding, and a number of compounds had been prepared prior to the preparation of the phosphorins which were analogous to the S-substituted thiabenzenes. 1,1-Diphenylphosphorin (46) is a yellow, non-crystalline compound, which shows a maximum absorption in the electronic spectrum at 409 nm. It appears to differ considerably in properties from the true phosphorins, and its electronic spectrum and reactivity to acids suggest that it has a ylide-like structure (e.g., 46b). The compound 47 in which phosphorus is hexacovalent,

has also been prepared and again has similar properties to 46.

The phosphorins themselves can be converted to P-substituted derivatives by oxidation. The oxidation of 44 with mercuric acetate in methanol gave the crystalline derivative 48, in which the phosphorus is pentavalent. The X-ray crystallographic analysis of 48 was similar to that for 44, but the

interesting point was noted that the main angle distortions occurred at positions 1, 3, and 5. The CPC angle was 107°, and the CCC angles at C-3 and C-5 were both 126°. The P-substituted phosphorin thus appears to have some delocalized stabilization.

Besides these 6 π-electron derivatives, all of the $4n$ or $4n + 2$ annulenes can, in principle, give the corresponding heterosystem by replacement of one carbon by a heteroatom. Azocine (**49**) is itself unknown, but a number of derivatives has been prepared. 2-Methoxy-1-azocine (**50**) is a yellow liquid, the nmr spectrum of which shows a 1H doublet at $\tau\,3.46$, a 4H multiplet at $\tau\,3.95$–4.25, and 1H multiplet at $\tau\,4.88$, all due to the ring protons, and a 3H singlet at $\tau\,6.30$ due to the methoxy group. The compound **50** thus appears to be localized, and presumably has a tub configuration similar to cyclooctatetraene. The azocines are readily reduced, both electrochemically and by alkali metals, to the corresponding planar dianions. This reduction

49   50

differs from that of cyclooctatetraene in that two discrete one-electron additions do not occur.

Neither azacyclodecapentaene (**51**), the 10 π-electron homologue of pyridine, nor any of the other heterocyclic annulene analogues, are at present known. However, a derivative of oxido[10]annulene, **51a**, containing

51   51a

a nitrogen atom in the 10-membered ring has recently been prepared, and this appears to be an aromatic system. In **51** itself, non-bonded interactions may still be important, but these should not intrude into the behaviour of the macrocyclic systems.

7.4   Systems with two heteroatoms

Potentially delocalized molecules with two heteroatoms can be classified in three types: (i) systems in which both heteroatoms replace carbon–carbon double bonds, (ii) systems in which both heteroatoms replace a carbon atom, and (iii) systems in which one heteroatom replaces a carbon–carbon double bond and the other a carbon atom. The three types are shown in Fig. 7.7. In the first type, both of the heteroatoms contribute 2 π-electrons to the delocalized system, and those compounds with odd numbers of double

Figure 7.7

bonds will have $4n + 2$ π-electrons, whereas those with even numbers of double bonds have $4n$ π-electrons. For the series shown in Fig. 7.8, 3,4-dithiacyclobutene has 6 π-electrons, 1,4-dithiin has 8 π-electrons, and 1,4-dithiacycloocta-2,5,7-triene has 10 π-electrons.

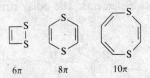

| 6π | 8π | 10π |

Figure 7.8

1,4-Dithiin (**52**) is an 8 π-electron system if both sulphur atoms contribute 2 π-electrons, whereas if one atom provides two and the other none, then a dipolar, 6 π-electron structure is formed (**53**). 1,4-Dithiin is a thermally stable

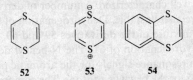

52　　　**53**　　　**54**

compound, unaffected by strong acids, but easily polymerized by Lewis acids. An X-ray crystallographic study showed that the molecule is a non-planar system, being in a boat conformation, with a CSC angle of 100° (Fig. 7.9). The bond lengths are within the range expected for normal C—S

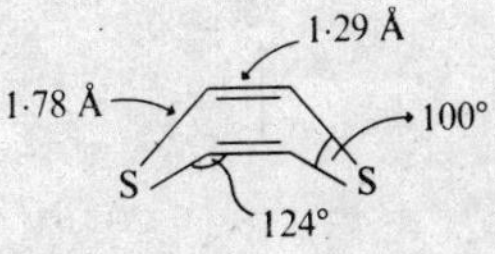

1·29 Å

1·78 Å　　　100°

S　　　S

124°

Figure 7.9

and C=C bonds. 1,4-Dithiin is thus a non-planar, non-aromatic molecule. By contrast the properties of benzo-1,4-dithiin (**54**) are more those expected for an aromatic molecule, this compound undergoing a variety of substitution reactions. 1,2-Dithiin has been prepared, and this is also nonaromatic. 3,4-Dithiacyclobutene and 1,4-dithiacyclooctatriene have not been synthesized.†

The replacement of a C=C unit in benzene by a B—N unit gives the isoelectronic, 6 π-electron borazarene (55), which is a type (ii) system. In this compound the nitrogen supplies two electrons to the π-system and the boron none, but the boron has an available atomic p-orbital for combination with the four carbon and nitrogen atomic orbitals. The nitrogen atom in borazarene is thus electron deficient, like the nitrogen of pyrrole, and the N—B bond is polarized in the reverse manner to that expected from the electronegativity of the two elements. The polar structure 56 indicates the

possible 'benzenoid' character of borazarene, and it might best be represented by 57. However, borazarene is an extremely unstable compound, which has not been well characterized. A number of derivatives are known, but most of these are also unstable. Dehydrogenation of 58 with palladium on charcoal gave a mixture of the derivatives 59 and 60, and 59 could also be prepared by dehydrogenation of 61. The N-benzyl derivative 60 shows in the nmr spectrum resonance signals for the aromatic protons at τ 2·3–2·8 and a singlet at τ 7·05 for the benzylic protons. The compound 60 is unstable, rapidly decomposing in air, whereas **59** is a relatively stable, crystalline solid. 2-Phenylborazarene (**59**) shows only aromatic protons (τ 2·2–3·7) in the nmr spectrum, and the ultraviolet spectrum resembles that of 2-phenyl-pyridine. The spectral properties of **59** and **60** thus suggest that these are delocalized systems, but the chemical properties indicate that these systems are far more reactive than the carbocyclic analogues.

More complex systems, such as 10,9-borazarophenanthrene (**62a**), are much more stable, and the derivatives **62a–c** resemble phenanthrene both in spectral and chemical properties. Thus the substituted compounds **62b** and **62c** readily undergo electrophilic substitution. Systems related to naphthalene and anthracene have also been prepared, and those compounds in which the boron and nitrogen atoms are adjacent are much more stable than those in which these atoms are separated (e.g., **63**).

62a R = H
62b R = OH
62c R = CH₃

63

The majority of the compounds of type (ii) have two carbon atoms replaced by two nitrogen atoms. The three analogues of benzene are pyridazine (**64**), pyrimidine (**65**), and pyrazine (**66**). Pyridazine is a liquid, m.p. −6°, while

64   65   66

pyrimidine and pyrazine are low melting solids. The dipole moments of these compounds decrease from 3·9D for **64**, through 2·4D for **65** to zero for **66**. All the compounds are less aromatic than pyridine or benzene, the hydroxyl substituted pyrimidines, for example, preferring to exist as the

67   68

keto rather than the enol tautomer (e.g., cytosine, $67 \rightleftharpoons 68$). This contrasts with the behaviour of resorcinol which exists primarily in the enolic form, maintaining the 6π-electron system.

Larger monocyclic ring systems containing two nitrogens are unknown, though attempts to prepare 1,6-diazo[10]annulene (**69**) have been reported. A derivative of a heterocyclic analogue of oxido[10]annulene, **69a**, has recently been prepared, and the nmr spectrum suggests that the 10-membered ring is delocalized. The synthesis of macrocyclic systems of this type would

69   **69a**

be of interest, particularly as porphin (**70**) may be considered to be a 1,10-diaza[18]annulene derivative. The [18]annulene ring is outlined in heavy lines in **70**, and in this system two nitrogen atoms each contribute one

70

electron, and the other two nitrogens and two of the double bonds are not involved in the delocalized system. The alternative tautomeric structure in which the nitrogen and double bonds reverse roles is also available.

There is a large number of examples of the third type of system with one heteroatom replacing a C═C and one a carbon atom. Many of these have 5-membered rings, and those with the C═C replaced by nitrogen are most common. In imidazole (**71**), the two nitrogens are equivalent, the N—H proton readily exchanging its position in the two tautomeric forms (**71a** $\rightleftharpoons$ **71b**). Imidazole undergoes electrophilic substitution, with the anion as the

71a   **71b**

134

reactive species. Thiazole (**72**) is a further stable system, and this molecule is readily quaternized to the corresponding thiazolium salt (e.g., **73**). The thiazolium salts have properties similar to the pyridinium salts, and the

position C-2 is acidic. Thiazole is not readily reduced, but it does give the 1:2 adduct **74** with dimethyl acetylenedicarboxylate, probably via a dipolar intermediate. A similar adduct can be obtained with pyridine.

These 5-membered ring systems appear to be delocalized molecules, which exhibit characteristic aromatic properties. The high homologues of these systems have so far not been investigated.

7.5 Systems with more than two heteroatoms

An enormous range of molecules with more than two heteroatoms is possible, and in general the extent of delocalization decreases with the increase in the number of heteroatoms. Only one type of system will be briefly considered here, the mesoionic compounds of which the sydnones were the first examples. The sydnones have the general formula **75**, and it can be seen from this formula that the atoms N-2 and C-4 do not have complete valency shells. A number of polar structures can be written, such as **76a, b** in which these valencies are satisfied, and in which the heterocyclic ring has an 'aromatic sextet'.

The sydnones do have a large dipole moment, in keeping with these dipolar structures, but in the nmr spectrum the proton at C-4 is a much higher field than would be expected for a system exhibiting a diamagnetic ring current. The sydnones are thermally stable, but they do react as 1,3-dipolar reagents, and add to acetylenes at elevated temperatures. The corresponding oxazolanes, such as **77**, called münchnones from their place of origin, are also mesoionic compounds. These are much more reactive than the sydnones, and are readily decomposed by moist air to the corresponding amino acid, e.g., **78**. The münchnones are certainly not aromatic in terms of the classical concept of lack of reactivity.

A wide range of heterocyclic systems are thus known which appear to have delocalized π-electron systems. At the present time those systems with 6 π-electrons have been by far the most extensively characterized, but recent interest in the 8 π and 10 π-electron systems suggests that a wider investigation of the other homologues will be undertaken. The extent of the applicability of Hückel's Rule to heteromonocyclic molecules may then be determined.

Further reading

Extensive accounts of the chemistry of heterocyclic systems are available including *Heterocyclic Compounds*, ed. R. C. Elderfield, Vols. 1–9, Wiley, and *Heterocyclic Compounds*, ed. A. Weissberger, Interscience.

For texts on the nitrogen heterocycles see K. Schofield, *Heteroaromatic Nitrogen Compounds*, Butterworths, London, 1967; A. Albert, *Heterocyclic Chemistry*, Athlone Press, London, 1968; L. A. Paquette, *Principles of Modern Heterocyclic Chemistry*, Benjamin, New York, 1968.

For the chemistry of the azepins and related systems see L. A. Paquette, in *Nonbenzenoid Aromatics*, ed. J. P. Snyder, Volume 1, Academic Press, New York, 1969.

For a review of pyrylium salts see A. T. Balaban, W. Schroth, and G. Fischer, in *Advances in Heterocyclic Chemistry*, 10, ed. A. R. Katritzky and A. J. Boulton, Interscience, New York, 1969.

For reviews of phosphorus heterocycles see G. Märkle, *Angew. Chem. Int. Ed.*, 1965, **4**, 1023; K. D. Berlin and D. M. Hellwege, *Topics in Phosphorus Chemistry*, 1969, **6**, 1.

For reviews of the boron heterocycles see M. J. S. Dewar in *Progress in Boron Chemistry*, ed. H. Steinberg and A. L. McLoskey, Pergamon, Oxford, 1964; M. F. Lappert in *The Chemistry of Boron and its Compounds*, ed. E. L. Muetterties, John Wiley, 1967; references to later work will be found in the paper by K. M. Davies, M. J. S. Dewar, and P. Rona, *J. Am. Chem. Soc.*, 1967, **89**, 6294.

For oxonin and related systems see S. Masamune, S. Takada, and R. T. Seidner, *J. Am. Chem. Soc.*, 1969, **91**, 7769; A. G. Anastassiou and J. H.

Gebrian, *Tetrahedron Letters*, 1970, 825; A. G. Anastassiou, R. P. Cellura, and J. H. Gebrian, *Chem. Commun.*, 1970, 375.

For azocine, see L. A. Paquette and T. Kakihana, *J. Am. Chem. Soc.*, 1971, **93**, 174, and references therein.

For the chemistry of mesoionic compounds see R. Huisgen, *Chemical Society Special Publication*, No 21, 1967, p. 51; M. Ohta and H. Kato in *Nonbenzenoid Aromatics*, ed. J. P. Snyder, Vol. 1, Academic Press, 1969.

For the recent synthesis of phosphabenzene and arsabenzene, see A. J. Ashe, *J. Am. Chem. Soc.*, **93**, 3293 (1971). For a recent synthesis of a 1,4-dithiacyclo-octatriene derivative see M. O. Riley and J. D. Park, *Tetrahedron Letters*, 1971, 2871.

8. Polycyclic systems

8.1 Introduction

The polycyclic systems present a number of problems which do not arise in monocyclic systems. Thus in monocyclic compounds if conjugation occurs it usually does so over the complete cycle, whereas polycyclic compounds may behave as if composed of individual discrete cycles, rather than as a single system. Counting the number of π-electrons, and applying the Hückel Rule cannot, in general, be expected to supply very meaningful predictions of the properties of polycyclic systems. Other simple methods, such as examining the number of π-electrons on the periphery, are also unlikely to be reliable for such predictions.

Another problem, partially arising out of the first, is how to classify polycyclic systems. Various classification schemes are possible, but only two will be considered in the present chapter. The first scheme is based on the π-electron properties of the component monocyclic rings. There are three types: (i) molecules formed by the fusion of two $4n + 2\kappa$-electron units, (ii) molecules formed by the fusion of two $4n$ π-electron units, and (iii) molecules formed by the fusion of a $4n$ and a $4n + 2$ π-electron unit. The molecules which result from (i) and (ii) have a total of $4n + 2$ π-electrons, whereas those resulting from (iii) have a total of $4n$ π-electrons. This classification system is tabulated in Table 8.1, and exemplified by the molecules shown in Fig. 8.1.

Systems of type (i), resulting from the fusion of two $4n + 2$ π-electron units, are well known, whereas systems belonging to types (ii) and (iii) have been much less investigated.

The other classification that will be used is to group together those molecules containing benzene rings as the benzenoid hydrocarbons, and those

Table 8.1

Type	Unit A	Unit B	Total no. of π-electrons
(i)	$4n + 2$	$4n + 2$	$4n + 2$
(ii)	$4n$	$4n$	$4n + 2$
(iii)	$4n + 2$	$4n$	$4n$

without such rings as the non-benzenoid hydrocarbons. Difficulties arise with this classification both in the case of compounds in which a benzene ring is merely annelated on to a non-benzenoid system, and also in those cases in which the benzenoid rings, although integral to the system, have

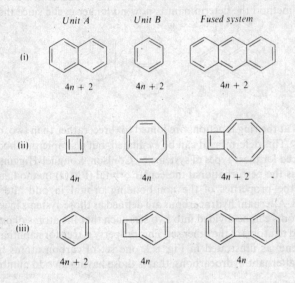

Figure 8.1

their properties greatly modified. Arbitrarily in the subsequent discussion the annelated systems will be classified as non-benzenoid, and the modified systems as benzenoid. In the subsequent sections the benzenoid molecules will be considered first, and these will be further classified to types (i), (ii), and (iii), wherever possible, and the non-benzenoid systems will then be treated in the same manner.

8.2 Benzenoid systems

Naphthalene (1) is conceptually formed by the fusion of two benzene molecules, and it is consequently a type (i) system with 10 π-electrons. Naphthalene is a white, crystalline solid (m.p. 80°), with a characteristic benzenoid electronic spectrum (see Fig. 8.5). It is diamagnetically anisotropic (see chapter 2), and the protons appear at low field in the nmr spectrum. Naphthalene undergoes electrophilic substitution, for example bromine gives 1-bromo- and 1,4- and 1,5-dibromonaphthalenes. It is unreactive towards dienophiles, only a low yield of the adduct 2 being obtained after prolonged reaction of 1 with maleic anhydride.

139

The physical and chemical properties of naphthalene are thus those expected for a classical aromatic system. In the Hückel Model the σ framework is fixed and each of the ten carbon atoms supplies one $2p$ orbital to the π-system. These are combined to give ten molecular orbitals, the energies of which can be determined by the HMO or more sophisticated methods. In the HMO method the determinant is now no longer cyclic since the two

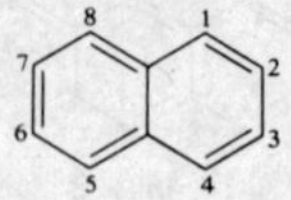

carbon atoms at the ring junctions are joined to three, rather than two, other carbon atoms. This determinant can be evaluated, but a simpler method has been introduced for these types of systems by Coulson, Longuet-Higgins and Dewar. This is the perturbational molecular orbital (PMO) method, and it is based on the properties of the non-bonding orbital in odd alternant hydrocarbons. Alternant hydrocarbons are defined as those systems in which the carbon atoms can be divided into two sets such that the atoms of one set are *only* joined to atoms of the other set. This property is true for naphthalene, but not azulene, as illustrated in Fig. 8.2, one set of carbon atoms being starred. Odd alternant hydrocarbons, that is those having an odd number of

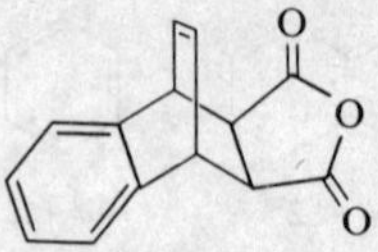

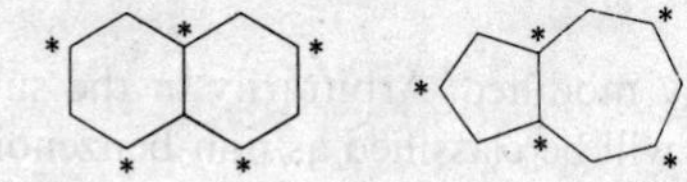

Figure 8.2

conjugated atoms, have a NBMO which has the property that there is zero electron density on one set of atoms, and the *sum* of the coefficients on the adjoining set of atoms is always zero. An estimate of the relative delocalization energies of naphthalene, [10]annulene, and decapentaene can.be determined by considering these molecules as being formed by addition of one carbon atom to the remaining nine-carbon-atom fragment. Both the one carbon atom and the nine carbon atoms are odd, alternant systems, and consequently have nonequal sets of alternant atoms. The larger set is starred, and the smaller set has zero electron density. The nine-carbon fragment is shown in Fig. 8.3 (i), and the coefficients of the NBMO in Fig. 8.3 (ii). The addition of the single carbon atom, which is the simplest odd alternant hydrocarbon, then introduces the perturbation effects shown in Fig. 8.3 (iii). The change in energy on the union of an odd alternant hydrocarbon with the single atom is given by eq. (8.1):

$$E = 2 \Sigma a\beta \qquad (8.1)$$

where a is the value of the coefficient at the carbon atom(s) to which the single carbon atom is joined, and β is the resonance integral. The change in

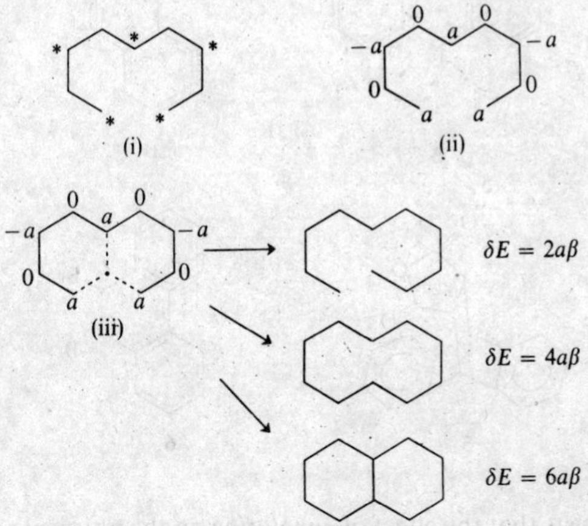

Figure 8.3

energy, δE, for decapentaene is $2a\beta$, for [10]annulene $4a\beta$, and for naphthalene $6a\beta$. The difference in energy between decapentaene and [10]annulene is thus $2a\beta$, and between decapentaene and naphthalene is $4a\beta$. These energy terms can then be equated to the delocalization energies of [10]annulene and naphthalene, and this suggests that besides removing the nonbonded interactions the transannular bond in naphthalene also leads to a system of lower energy.

The PMO method is very simple and provides a useful indication of the probable gain in stability to be expected for a cyclic or polycyclic system when compared to the acyclic analogue. The theoretical justification for the PMO method has been fully discussed by Dewar (see chapter 1, Further Reading), and the method will be used throughout the remainder of this chapter.

Anthracene (**3**) and phenanthrene (**4**) are conceptually formed by the fusion of a third benzene ring to naphthalene, and these molecules are thus type (i) systems. Both are white, crystalline solids, with benzenoid electronic spectra (Fig. 8.5). However, besides typical aromatic behaviour, such as electrophilic substitution, both molecules undergo reactions which are typical of unsaturated, rather than aromatic, systems. Thus anthracene smoothly reacts with maleic anhydride to give the Diels–Alder adduct **5**, and phenanthrene adds bromine across the 9,10-double bond to give **6**.

The decrease in aromatic character observed in the addition of a further ring to naphthalene has been developed into a general theory by Clar.

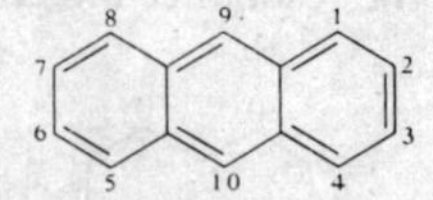

3

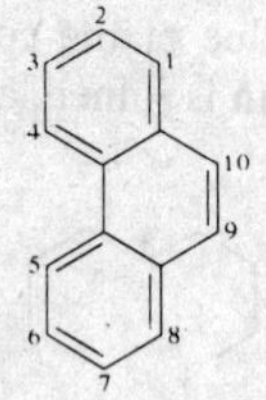

4

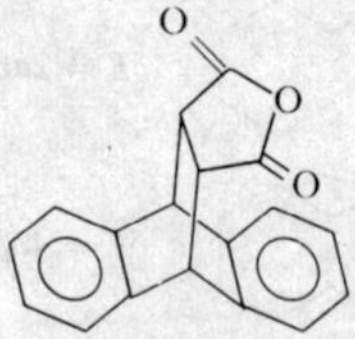

5

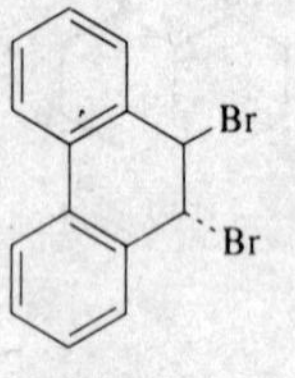

6

This theory suggests that the effect of *annelation* on the physical and chemical properties of a system will depend on the number of aromatic sextets that can be formed. The aromatic sextets are depicted by the circle notation, which is used as in its original formulation by Armit and Robinson, rather than the more common usage merely to depict delocalization. Any π-electrons which do not participate in aromatic sextets are shown as double bonds (Fig. 8.4). The formulae in Fig. 8.4 depict only one possible ' sextet ' structure

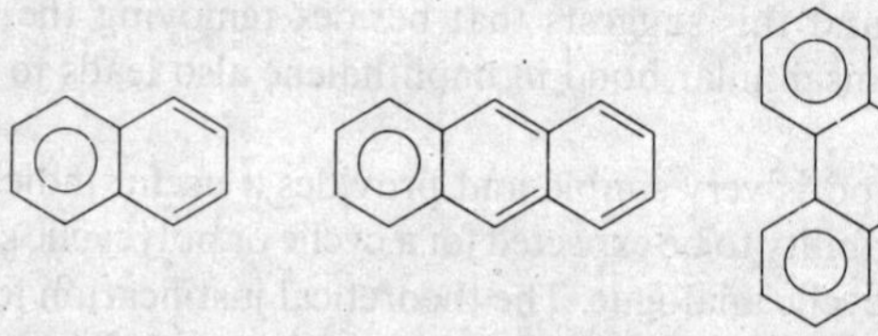

Figure 8.4

for these systems, and the sextet can be drawn in any of the six-membered rings. In the case of phenanthrene, the formula with the central ring containing the aromatic sextet has both the other rings polyenic, and this emphasizes the reactivity of the 9,10-bond. Converting anthracene to the Diels–Alder adduct **6**, gives a system with two aromatic sextets. The changes in the electronic spectra of these systems were correlated by Clar, who established that these absorption bands arose from the same transitions as those in benzene. These electronic spectra are shown in Fig. 8.5, and it can be seen that each compound has three main absorption bands, and that the effect of annelation in any series is to cause a bathochromic shift to higher wavelengths. The large polycyclic systems are coloured, the colours changing from yellow through red to blue with increased annelation.

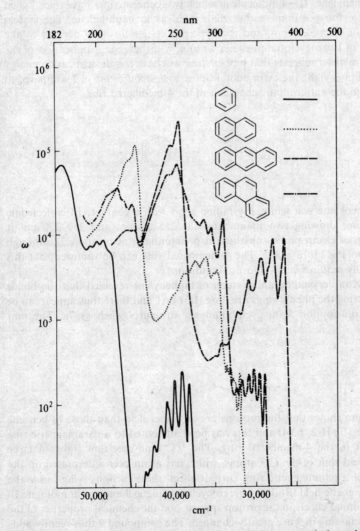

Figure 8.5 Electronic spectra of benzene, naphthalene, anthracene, and phenanthrene in hexane (adapted from spectra due to H.-H. Perkampus and G. Kassebeer, and E. M. F. Roe in the *DMS U.V. Atlas*, Butterworths, 1966).

Although the concept of annelation gives good correlations between the properties of the various compounds, it should be used with caution. Thus the nmr spectrum of anthracene reveals that the 9,10-protons are not deshielded, appearing at $\tau\,1\cdot69$, and the 9,10-protons of phenanthrene, although appearing at highest field in the nmr spectrum, are still in the aromatic region ($\tau\,2\cdot29$), at lower field than the protons of benzene.

Biphenylene (7) is a molecule in which two benzene rings have to be joined in the ortho positions, rather than fused as in naphthalene. The system contains 12 π-electrons, and is a type (iii) system formally derived by the fusion of benzocyclobutadiene, a $4n$ unit, with benzene. Application of the PMO method suggests that biphenylene will have *less* delocalization energy than diphenyl (8), the extra bond leading to *destabilization* of 7 compared to 8 due to the antiaromatic character of the 4-membered ring.

7   8

Biphenylene is a white, crystalline solid with a characteristic electronic spectrum, showing two main bands at 235–260 nm and 330–370 nm. It undergoes electrophilic substitution preferentially at position 2, although position 1 is more acidic. The 4-membered ring can be ruptured, but this normally requires fairly vigorous conditions.

An X-ray crystallographic study of biphenylene revealed that the bonds connecting the phenyl rings are long (1·514 Å), and there thus appears to be little contribution from cyclobutadiene structures, such as 7a. The nmr

7a

spectrum shows that the protons are at higher field than those of benzene (H-1, $\tau\,3\cdot3$; H-2, $\tau\,3\cdot4$) and this has been attributed to a paramagnetic ring current in the 4-membered ring. The ^{13}C nmr spectrum shows a large downfield shift of the C-3 atoms, which has again been interpreted on the basis of a paramagnetic ring current effect, these carbons lying *inside* the paramagnetic field. Both the heterocyclic analogue 9 and the homologue 10 show similar effects in the proton spectra, and the chemical properties of the thiophene ring in 9 are greatly changed. The compound 9 thus readily adds bromine to the thiophene ring, and on oxidation it gives a dioxide which does not dimerize. The general properties of the compounds 7, 9, and 10 suggest that the formation of a benzocyclobutadiene structure is an unfavoured process.

9   10

Phenalene (11) is a member of an interesting group of compounds, which on oxidation give potentially delocalized systems for which no Kekulé structure can be written. The chemical properties of phenalene indicate that it is difficult to designate any one of the rings as non-aromatic, as rapid inter-conversion occurs in substituted phenalene between structures in which different rings are aromatic. Phenalene is readily converted into the anion, cation, or free radical, all of these systems being best represented as having

11   12   13

12 π-electron periphery, with the charge or odd electron on the central carbon atom (e.g., 12).

Another example of this type of system is triangulene (13), which is pre-dicted by m.o. calculations to be a triplet diradical, but this compound is, at present, unknown.

The phenalene type systems are not readily classified by the method dis-cussed in section 8.1, and another molecule which does not fit easily into this classification is corannulene (14). This consists of five fused benzene rings and the molecule has a total of 20 π-electrons. However, the canonical structure 14b suggests that the molecule might behave as a fulvalene with a 14 π-electron periphery. Corannulene readily forms the corannulene radical anion 15, with the central system as the cyclopentadienyl anion and a 15 π-electron peripheral radical.

14   14b   15

145

A number of polycyclic systems have been prepared, which might be considered as annelated annulenes. An example is the molecule 16, which appears as a hexaphenyl [18]annulene. However, for conjugation to occur in the macrocyclic ring the benzenoid conjugation must be disrupted, and 16 does not have any properties to suggest extended conjugation.

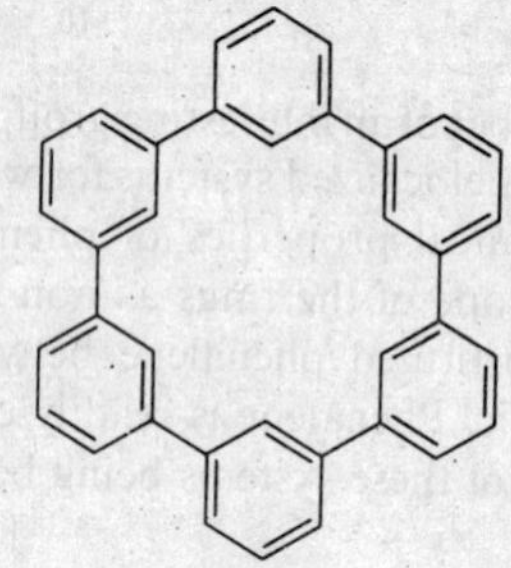

16

8.3 Non-benzenoid systems

Interest in non-benzenoid polycyclic systems was stimulated by some early HMO calculations of Brown, who predicted that pentalene (17) and heptalene (18) should have a considerable delocalization energy. Subsequent

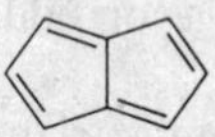

17 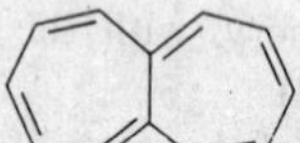   18

valence bond and more extensive molecular orbital calculations suggested that the structures with localized double bonds would be more stable, and the PMO method agrees with these results. As is shown in Fig. 8.6, the PMO

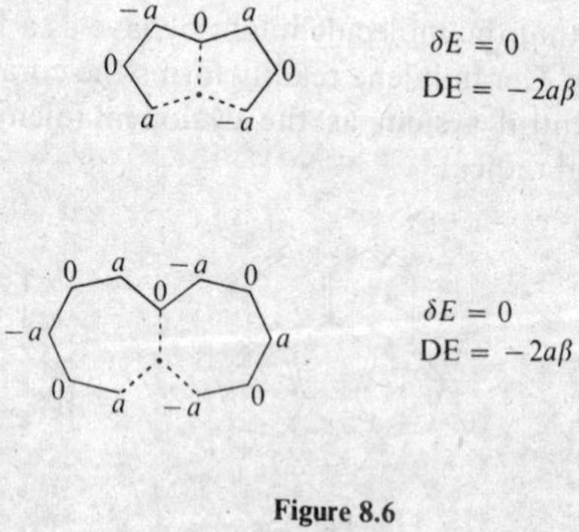

$$\delta E = 0$$
$$DE = -2a\beta$$

$$\delta E = 0$$
$$DE = -2a\beta$$

Figure 8.6

method predicts that both pentalene and heptalene are *antiaromatic* systems, the transannular bond not contributing to the stabilization of these compounds, which can be considered as slightly perturbed forms of cyclooctatetraene and [12]annulene respectively.

Although attempts to prepare pentalene have so far been unsuccessful, the syntheses of 1,3-bis(dimethylamino)pentalene (19) and hexaphenylpentalene (20) have been reported. The compound 19 is a dark blue, crystalline solid, which is stable to oxygen at 20° for several hours. The nmr spectrum consists of an A_2B system, composed of a two-proton doublet at τ 4·31 (H-4, H-6) and a one-proton singlet at τ 4·66 (H-5), a twelve-proton singlet at τ 6·92 (N(CH$_3$)$_2$), and a one-proton singlet at τ 7·20 due to the ' enamine ' proton H-2. The dipolar structure 19b appears to make a major contribution

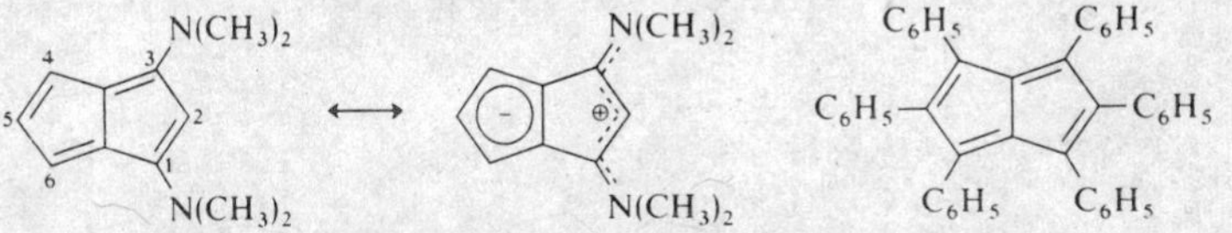

19a   19b   20

to the ground state of the system. Hexaphenylpentalene is a stable, crystalline solid, which has a complex electronic spectrum similar to that of 19.

Heptalene (18) was prepared by Dauben and Bertelli by the route shown in Fig. 8.7. The ditosylate 21 was ring expanded by solvolysis in a mixture of acetic acid, NaH$_2$PO$_4$ to give the dihydroheptalene 22. Hydride abstraction with trityl fluoroborate gave the heptalenium cation 23, which on deprotonation gave heptalene.

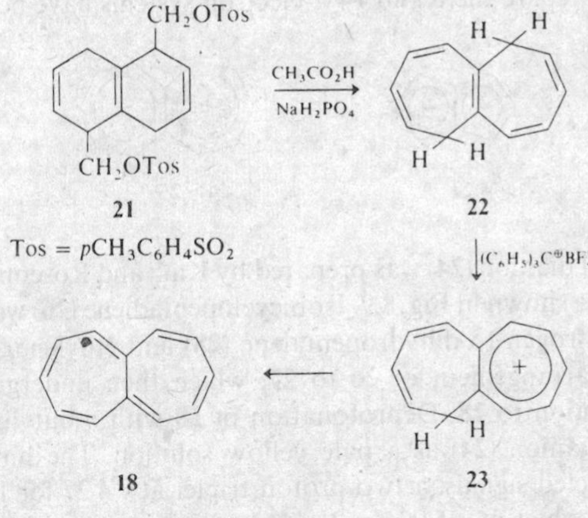

21

Tos = pCH$_3$C$_6$H$_4$SO$_2$

18   23

Figure 8.7

147

Heptalene is a reddish-brown liquid which is rapidly polymerized by oxygen or by warming to 50°. The electronic spectrum has bands at 265 and 352 nm, and the nmr spectrum shows resonance signals centred at $\tau\,4.2$ and 4.9. The spectral properties and the lack of diamagnetic exaltation, indicate that heptalene is not a delocalized system.

Although pentalene and heptalene thus appear to be non-aromatic, or even antiaromatic compounds, both could, in principle, be converted to aromatic systems by the addition or removal of two electrons. Of the four possible doubly charged ions, the two with 10 π-electrons are type (i) systems, and the other two are type (ii) systems. The four ions are shown in Fig. 8.8.

Figure 8.8

At the present time only one of these ions, the pentalenyl dianion (**24**), a type (i) system derived from the fusion of two 6π electron cyclopentadienyl anions, has been prepared. Attempts to prepare the second 10 π-electron system, the heptalenium dication (**25**) have so far proved unsuccessful, and no attempts to prepare the 6 and 14 π-electron systems have been reported.

The pentalenyl dianion (**24**) was prepared by Katz and Rosenberger by the reaction sequence shown in Fig. 8.9. Isobicyclopentadiene (**26**) was pyrolysed at 575° under nitrogen to dihydropentalene (**28**) and ethylene, presumably via an initial rearrangement of **26** to **27**, which then undergoes a retro-Diels–Alder reaction to **28**. Deprotonation of **28** with n-butyllithium gave the pentalenyl dianion (**24**) as a pale yellow solution. The nmr spectrum showed the expected signals, a two-proton triplet at $\tau\,4.27$ for H[2], H[5], and a four-proton doublet at $\tau\,5.02$ for the remaining protons. The high field position of these protons reflects the high negative charge density which offsets the deshielding effect of the diamagnetic ring current. The pentalene dianion is related to pentalene in exactly the same way as the cyclooctatetraene dianion is related to cyclooctatetraene (chapter 4).

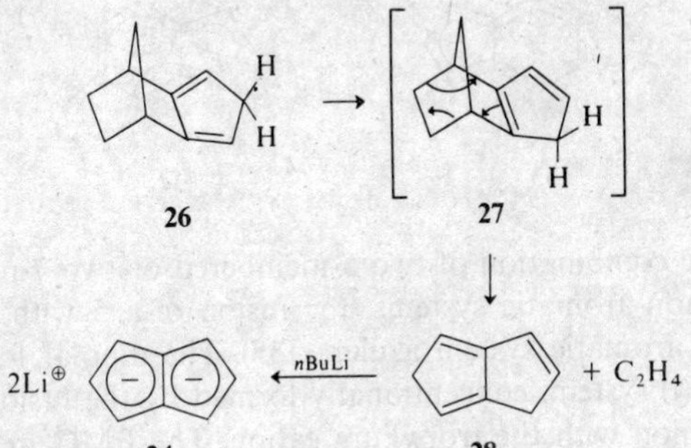

Figure 8.9

Two systems that are closely related to pentalene are the s- and as-indacenes. Of these two systems, s-indacene (**29**) has been prepared, but as-indacene (**30**) is at present unknown. Both compounds have a 12 π-electron periphery, and can be considered as perturbed [12]annulenes. s-Indacene is a red oil which is thermally labile and susceptible to oxidation. Mild hydrogenation

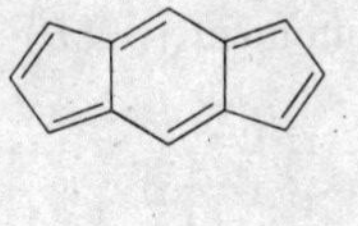

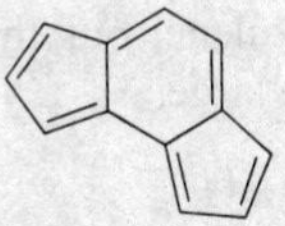

converts **29** into s-hydrindacene (**31**), and bromination gives hexabromo-s-hydrindacene (**32**), emphasizing the tendency of the central ring to become benzenoid.

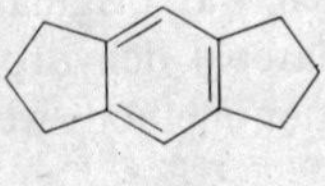

The reduction of **29** and **30** to the corresponding dianions would give type (i) systems containing 14 π-electrons, while the corresponding dications would be type (ii) systems containing 10 π-electrons. Both the dianions **33**

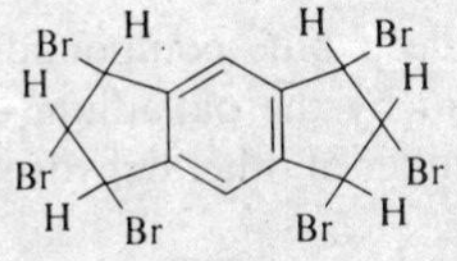

149

and **34** have been prepared as air-sensitive salts which on treatment with water give the corresponding dihydroindenes. The nmr spectrum of **34** is consistent with this molecule being a planar, delocalized system.

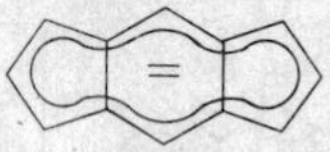

33 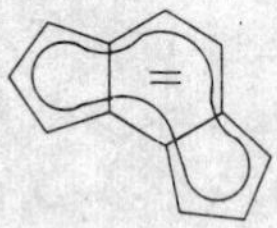   34

Whereas the combination of two 5-membered or two 7-membered rings gives rise to non-aromatic systems, the fusion of a 5 with a 7-membered ring gives the aromatic system azulene (**35**). The dipolar form of azulene, **35b**, is a type (i) system, conceptionally formed by the fusion of the cyclopentadienyl anion with the tropylium cation. The PMO method indicates

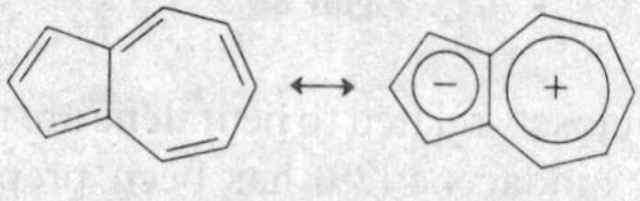

35a   35b

that azulene will have the same delocalization energy as [10]annulene, the transannular bond being a minor perturbation (Fig. 8.10). The dipolar structure **35b** might be expected to make a significant contribution to the ground state of azulene, but the dipole moment ($1.08D$) suggests that its contribution is not large.

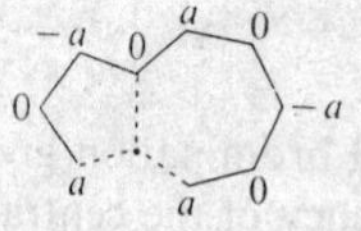

$$\delta E = 4a\beta$$
$$DE = 2a\beta$$

Figure 8.10

Azulene is a deep blue compound, which was originally prepared by Plattner and Pfau by the palladium on charcoal dehydrogenation of the alcohol **36**. A number of other dehydrogenation methods were subsequently

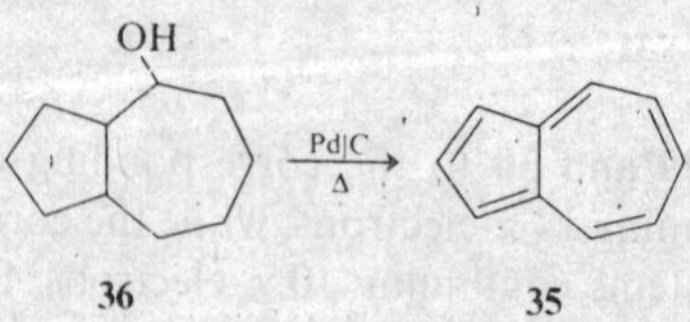

36   35

derived, but a much superior synthesis which does not involve dehydrogenation is outlined in Fig. 8.11. The salt **37**, which is readily prepared by
treatment of N-(2,4-dinitrophenyl)pyridine with N-methylaniline reacts with

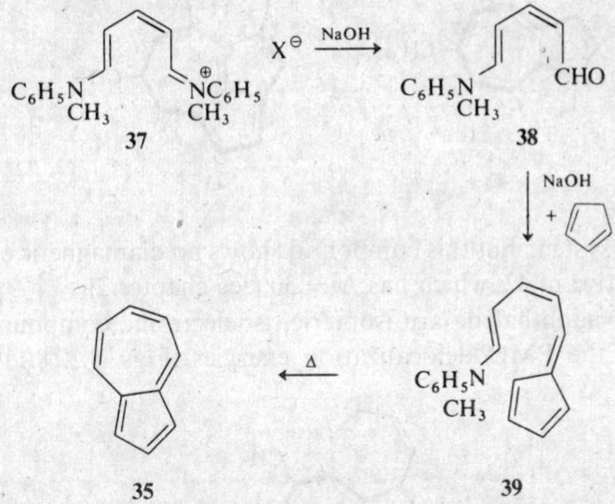

Figure 8.11

base to give the aldehyde **38**. Condensation of **38** with cyclopentadiene gives
the fulvene **39**, which on pyrolysis gives azulene.

Azulene is readily protonated, the proton adding in the 1-position of the
cyclopentadiene ring to form the azulenium cation **40**. Electrophilic substitution also occurs at this position, whereas nucleophilic substitution
takes place in the 7-membered ring, presumably via the intermediate **41**.
The reactions of azulene are thus controlled by the formation of new
6 π-electron systems during the course of the reaction.

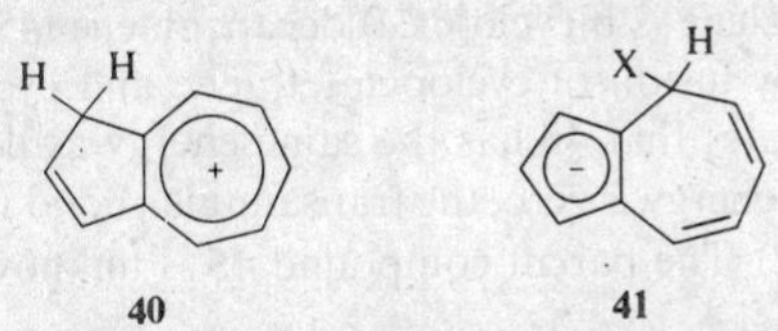

A number of polycyclic systems have been prepared containing a number
of 5 and 7-membered rings. The tricyclic system **42** can be considered to be
either a derivative of pentalene or azulene. The nmr spectrum and chemical
properties indicate that **42** is best considered to be an azulene with an
exocyclic double bond. The tetracyclic system **43** may be considered to be a
derivative of either pentalene, heptalene, or azulene. The spectral and chemical properties are, however, best interpreted on the basis that **43** has a

151

14 π-electron periphery, and a central double bond. The tricyclic system **44** is again best considered to be an azulene derivative with the addition of an

42   43

exocyclic diene system, but this compound shows no diamagnetic exaltation, unlike a derivative of **42**, which has $\Lambda = 30$ (see chapter 2).

Azulene and naphthalene are isomeric, isoelectronic compounds, but a comparison of the PMO delocalization energies (Figs. 8.3, 8.11) indicate

44

that whereas the transannular bond in naphthalene stabilizes the system, that in azulene acts only as minor perturbation. This finding is supported by the X-ray crystallographic analysis of azulene, which indicates that the central bond is long. The fact that azulene is aromatic, whereas [10]annulene is not, appears to be due to the removal of nonbonded interactions in the former compound. A third system which is isomeric and isoelectronic with azulene and naphthalene is bicyclo[6.2.0]decapentaene (**45**), which is a type (ii) system formed by fusion of cyclooctatetraene and cyclobutadiene. The PMO method indicates that **45** has the same energy as decapentaene, that is the delocalization energy is zero, the transannular bond in fact destabilizes the system (Fig. 8.12). The parent compound **45** is unknown, but a number

45

of substituted derivatives have been prepared (**46a–c**). These are rather unstable compounds, and the nmr spectrum of **46a** shows a singlet at τ 3·1 for the cyclobutenyl proton, and a multiplet centred at τ 4·0 for the protons

152

on the eight-membered ring. The compounds **46a–c** react with tetracyano-ethylene to give mixtures of the 2 + 2 adducts **47a–c** and **48a–c**. The benzan-nelated derivative **49** is a crystalline solid, and again the spectral and chemical

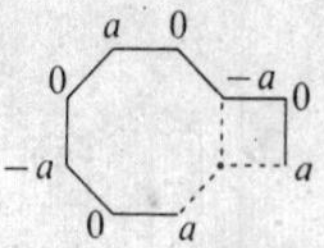

$$\delta E = 2a\beta$$

$$DE = 0$$

Figure 8.12

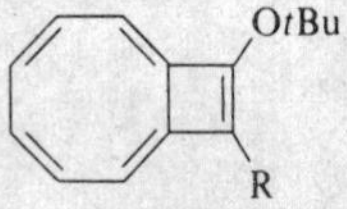

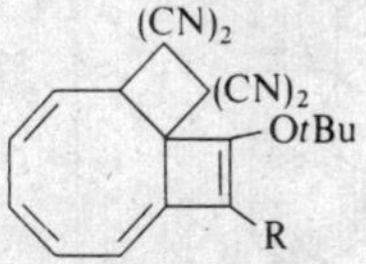

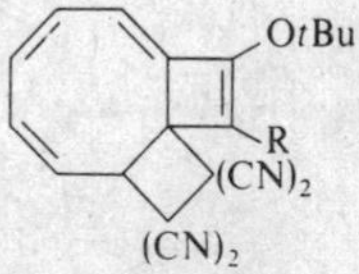

46a R = H	**47a** R = H	**48a** R = H
46b R = O*t*Bu	**47b** R = O*t*Bu	**48b** R = O*t*Bu
46c R = Cl	**47c** R = Cl	**48c** R = Cl

properties indicate that the 8-membered ring is a nonplanar, non-delocalized system. The bicyclo[6.2.0]decapentaene system is therefore non-aromatic, and the properties of the individual rings dominate the properties of the system.

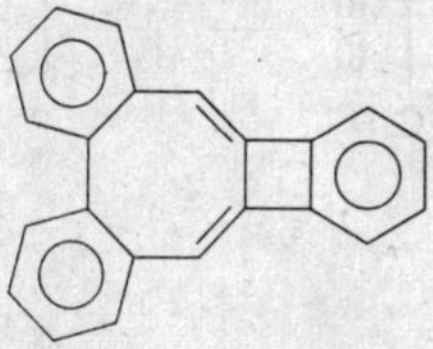

49

Benzocyclobutadiene (**51**) is known only as a transient intermediate in a number of chemical reactions. Debromination of 1,2-dibromobenzocyclo-butene (**50**) with zinc powder generates benzocyclobutadiene (**51**), which dimerizes in a Diels–Alder manner via **52** to give the dihydrobenzobi-phenylene **53** (Fig. 8.13). The PMO method actually indicates that the transannular bond stabilizes benzocyclobutadiene as compared to planar cyclooctatetraene, benzocyclobutadiene being non-aromatic rather than antiaromatic (Fig. 8.14).

Although no benzocyclobutadienes have been isolated, a number of naphthocyclobutadiene and anthrocyclobutadiene derivatives have been prepared. 1,2-Diphenylnaphthocyclobutadiene (56) was obtained by debromination of the dibromide 55. The nmr spectrum of 56 shows, besides the

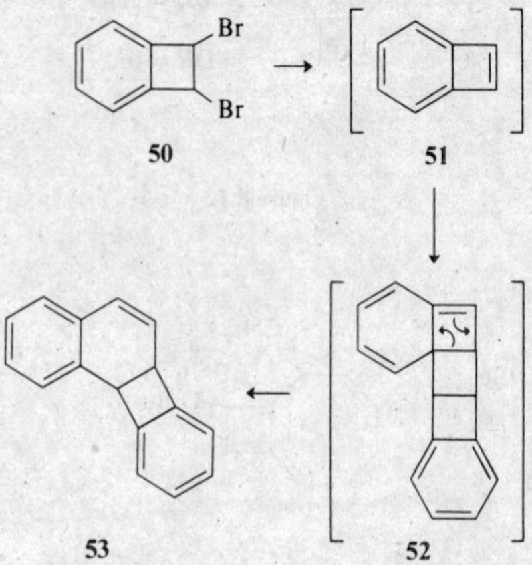

Figure 8.13

aromatic protons, a two-proton singlet at τ 3.5 due to the H^a protons. The compound 56 reacts with 1,3-diphenylisobenzofuran (57) to form the Diels–Alder adduct 58. The naphthocyclobutadienes are presumably more stable

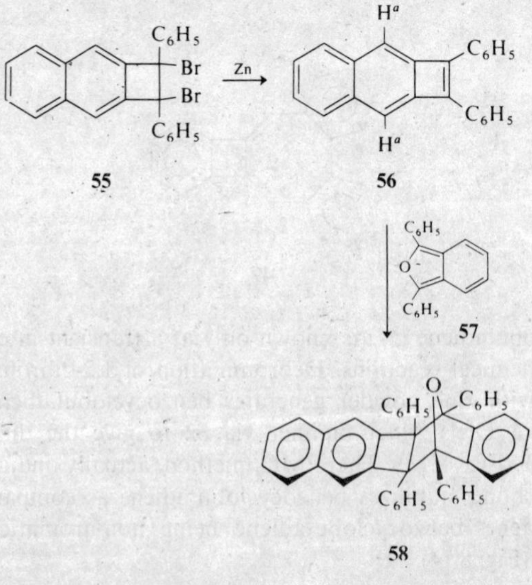

154

than the benzocyclobutadienes in that the canonical form **56a** can predominate with the loss of only one aromatic sextet. The parent naphtho-

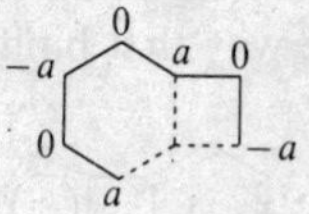

$$\delta E = 2a\beta$$
$$DE = 0$$

Figure 8.14

cyclobutadiene has itself only been implicated as a transient intermediate, and it appears necessary for the stabilization of the cyclobutadiene that the 4-membered ring should be fully substituted.

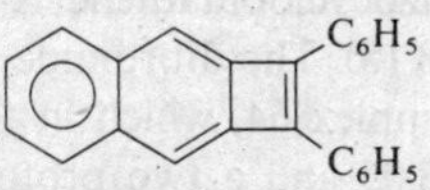

56a

The fact that the cyclobutadiene ring actually destabilizes these types of systems has recently been emphasized by Breslow and his co-workers. The hydroquinone **59** is an unstable compound which slowly dimerizes. On electrochemical oxidation **59** gives the quinone **60** which is even less stable than **59**. The oxidation of **59** to **60** was shown to occur less readily than the oxidation of naphthohydroquinone to naphthoquinone, whereas, the dihydro compound **61** was oxidized more readily than naphthohydroquinone. An estimate of *ca* 12 kcal.mole^{-1} was made for the *destabilizing* effect of the double bond.

In a related series, it has been observed that the bicyclo[3.2.0]heptatrienyl anion (**62**) and the norbiphenylene anion (**63**) are both much less stable than

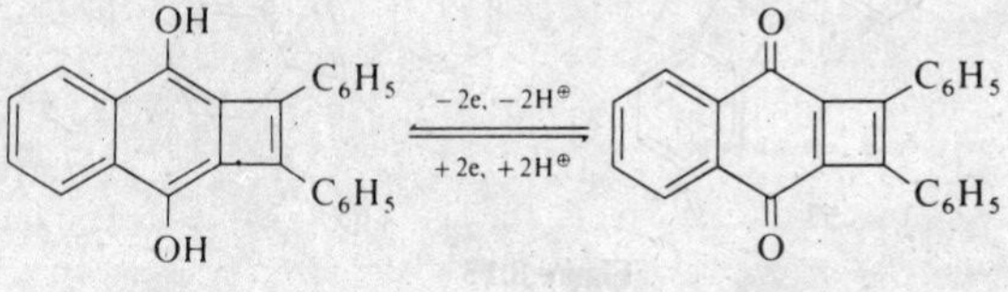

59   60

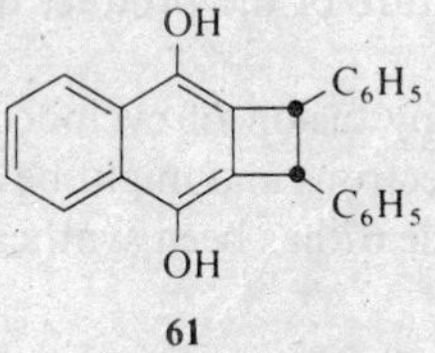

61

the cyclopentadienyl anion. The anion **62** can be considered to be a perturbed cycloheptatrienyl anion, and **63** as a benzannelated derivative of this system. It has been estimated that **62** is about 15 kcal.mole^{-1} *less* thermodynamically stable than the cyclopentadienyl anion. The anion **63** is presumably somewhat more stable than **62** in the same way that biphenylene is more stable

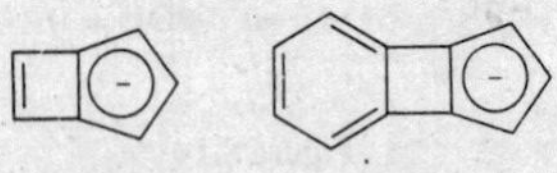

62   **63**

than benzocyclobutadiene. The rather artificial nature of the classification scheme is apparent here, as biphenylene, which was discussed in section 8.2, might more readily be considered to be a non-benzenoid system.

Like cyclobutadiene, benzocyclobutadiene is stabilized by complexing with iron tricarbonyl (Fig. 8.15). The dibromide **50** on treatment with iron enneacarbonyl gives the complex **64**, which in the nmr spectrum shows a four proton multiplet at τ 3.05 and a two proton singlet at τ 5.98 for the aromatic and cyclobutadienyl protons, respectively. Oxidative removal of

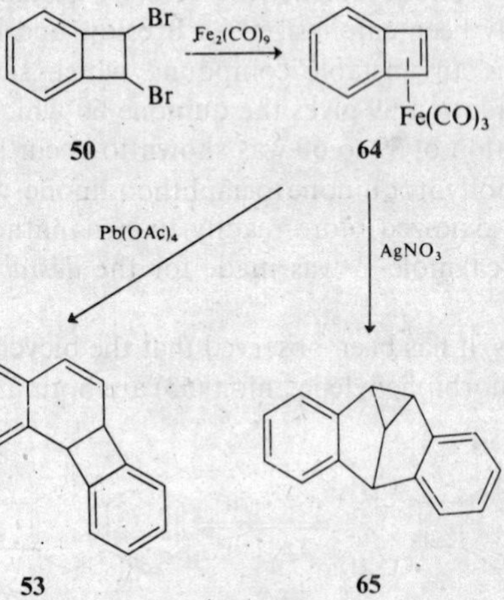

Figure 8.15

the iron group leads to dimerization, the nature of the product depending upon the oxidizing agent used.

The cation **66**, a type (ii) system formed by fusion of cyclooctatetraene with a cyclopentadienium cation, has 10 π-electrons and might be aromatic. Although **66** has not been prepared, the ketone **67** has been synthesized, and this shows no aromatic properties.

Octalene (**68**) is another type (ii) system formed by the fusion of two cyclo-octatetraene rings, and it has 14 π-electrons. However, the PMO method

predicts that the molecule has no delocalization energy and is less stable than [14]annulene. Octalene itself has not been synthesized, but benzo-octalene (**69**) and furooctalene (**70**) have been prepared, and from the spectral

and chemical properties these are non-planar, localized systems, the eight-membered rings probably having the tub conformation. Hexabenzooctalene (**71**) has also been prepared and appears to be a non-aromatic, non-planar molecule.

8.4 Conclusion

In only the type (i) systems are the properties of the individual rings consistent with the theoretical properties of the overall number of π-electrons. In both the type (ii) and type (iii) systems the properties of the individual rings are different from those expected for the total number of π-electrons, and it appears that in these molecules it is the properties of the individual rings that are important. If systems are to be discovered in which the total number of π-electrons is dominant, these will probably be systems in which delocalization of charge will favour the extended conjugation. It appears that the

PMO method is particularly useful in its application to polycyclic systems, and it is preferable to making simple HMO calculations in such systems.

Further reading

For a discussion of the benzenoid polycyclic hydrocarbons see E. Clar, *Polycyclic Hydrocarbons*, Volumes 1 and 2, Academic Press, 1964; and for non-benzenoid polycyclic systems see *Advances in Organic Chemistry*, Volume **6**, p. 1.

For a discussion of biphenylene and similar systems, see M. P. Cava and M. J. Mitchell, *Cyclobutadiene and Related Compounds*, Academic Press, 1967, and J. W. Barton, in *Nonbenzenoid Aromatics*, Volume 1, ed. J. P. Snyder, Academic Press, 1969.

For a review of some complex polycyclic systems see K. Hafner, *Angew. Chem. Intern. Ed. Engl.*, 1964, **3**, 165.

For recent work in the benzocyclobutadiene area see R. Breslow, R. Grubbs, and S.-I. Murahashi, *J. Am. Chem. Soc.*, 1970, **92**, 4139, and P. J. Garratt and K. P. C. Vollhardt, *Angew. Chem. Intern. Ed. Engl.*, 1971, **10**, 125, and the reference in these papers.

For a recent synthesis of 1-methylpentalene see R. Bloch, R. A. Marty, and P. de Mayo, *J. Am. Chem. Soc.*, **93**, 3071 (1971).

9. Homoaromatic and bicycloaromatic systems

In the preceding chapters a wide variety of compounds has been discussed, the main link between them being that the possibility existed that complete delocalization of the π-electrons over all of the annular atoms could occur. In the present chapter a group of compounds will be examined in which such delocalization is interrupted by one or more saturated atoms. The general question to be answered will remain the same, however: can the energy of the system be lowered by cyclic delocalization of the π-electrons over the remaining atoms?

The first suggestion that delocalization might occur in such a system was advanced by Thiele to explain the decreased acidity of the methylene protons in cycloheptatriene compared to those in cyclopentadiene. Thiele postulated that a 1,6-interaction in cycloheptatriene (1) would give a benzene-like system, and that this ' aromatic character ' would be lost on deprotonation, which therefore does not occur. Although this is not currently the accepted

explanation for the difference in acidity between cycloheptatriene and cyclopentadiene, nevertheless the occurrence of such an interaction in cycloheptatriene has found a number of supporters. Of particular interest is the observation by Dauben and his co-workers that the diamagnetic exaltation (Λ) is 8·1 for cycloheptatriene, which they suggest is only consistent with cycloheptatriene possessing a partially delocalized structure. In their earlier studies on the Buchner acids, von Doering and his collaborators had suggested that a similar interaction in these compounds would best explain the observed properties. These investigators showed that there were only four Buchner acids (2), corresponding to the four possible isomers with the carboxylic acid function at positions 1, 2, 3, and 7, and the suggestion was made that the properties were best explained by these acids having planar, aromatic structures due to the 1,6-interaction, which was illustrated by structure 3. Although the cycloheptatrienes are in fact now known to be non-planar, the results of Dauben and others seem to indicate that the 1,6-interaction is still appreciable.

Winstein and his co-workers attempted to observe this type of interaction in 1,4,7-cyclononatriene (4), which might be considered to be benzene with three interrupting methylene groups, as shown in formula 5. The term

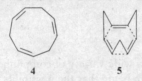

4   5

' homoaromatic ' was introduced to describe the phenomenon of interrupted delocalization, and the structure 5 then represents trishomobenzene. The properties of 4 do not suggest that 5 makes any contribution to the structure.

The most convincing cases of homoaromatic participation have arisen from a study of potentially homoaromatic ions. The homotropylium cation (7) was first prepared by von Rosenberg, Mahler, and Pettit in 1962, by treatment of cyclooctatetraene (6) with concentrated sulphuric acid or with $SbCl_5$ and HCl in nitromethane. The hexachloroantimonate of 7 has a complex nmr spectrum, showing a multiplet at τ 1·5 (H^2, H^3, H^4, H^5, H^6), a

$$\xrightarrow[CH_3NO_2]{HCl, SbCl_5}$$

6   7

multiplet at τ 3·4 (H^1, H^7) and multiplets at τ 4·8 and 10·6 due to H^b and H^a respectively. The nmr spectrum is best accommodated by the open structure 7, in which one of the methylene protons is above and inside the ring (H^a), while the other is above and outside (H^b). The classical structure 8 would be expected to have H-1, H-7 at higher field (ca τ 7·0 rather than τ 3·4), and a larger coupling between the cis protons H^b and H^1 than between the $trans$ protons H^a and H^1. In fact the coupling between H^a and H^1 (10 Hz) is greater than that between H^b and H^1 (7·5 Hz). Structure 7 has been further substantiated by a recent nmr study at 251 MHz at which frequency the constants between all coupled protons were evaluated and found to have the expected values for structure 7. The difference in chemical shift between H^a and H^b can be attributed to the effect of the diamagnetic ring current in 7, which shields the inner and deshields the outer proton.

The π-orbitals which must participate in the formation of the seven molecular orbitals are shown diagramatically in Fig. 9.1. The orbital overlap

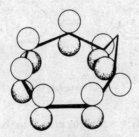

8

between C-1 and C-7 occurs through only one lobe of the π-atomic orbital, and this partially resembles a σ type bond. However, the structure **7** appears to be a better representation of the homotropylium cation than **8**.

Figure 9.1

Simple HMO calculations can be made for the homotropylium cation by treating it as a tropylium cation and adjust the values of the resonance integral across the 1,6-atoms. Using a value for this integral $\beta_{1,7} = 0.5\beta$, Winstein calculated that the delocalization energy for the homotropylium cation was 2.423β, compared to 2.988β for the tropylium cation itself.

The ultraviolet spectrum of **7** is quite similar to that of the tropylium ion, having absorption bands at 232·5 nm ($\log \varepsilon\ 4.52$) and 313 nm ($\log \varepsilon\ 3.48$). These bands show a bathochromic shift compared to those of the tropylium cation, but the spectrum is very different from that of the heptatrienyl cation. A resonance integral of 0.73β must be assumed to predict the positions of the long-wavelength band by an HMO calculation, but such calculations are not very reliable. A measurement of the diamagnetic exaltation of **7** gave a value of Λ of 18, a value of the same order as those for benzene and the tropylium cation, and again in accord with **7** being a delocalized compound.

When the homotropylium cation is prepared by treatment with D_2SO_4 below $-15°$, then it is found that 80 per cent of the deuterium is incorporated in the *endo*-position (Fig. 9.2). The deuterium thus adds to cyclooctatetraene from a position inside the ring. On warming the solution equilibrium occurs between the *endo* and *exo* positions, presumably via a ring inversion (*7-endo-d* ⇌ *7-exo-d*) through the planar cation **9** (for the inversion of cyclooctatetraene, see chapter 2). This equilibration occurs on the nmr time scale, and the

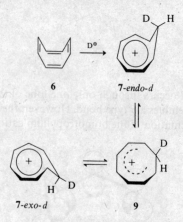

Figure 9.2

barrier to inversion ($\Delta G^{\ddagger}$) was determined to be 22·3 kcal.mol^{-1}. This barrier height may then be assumed to be equivalent to the *gain* in delocalization energy on going from the cyclooctatrienyl cation **9** to the homotropylium cation **7**.

A number of transition metal complexes of this cation have been prepared which nicely illustrate the balance between the electronic requirements of the metal and those of the ligand. The molybdenum tricarbonyl (**10**) and tungsten tricarbonyl (**11**) complexes have the ligand in the open, delocalized form found in the non-complexed cation **7**, whereas the iron tricarbonyl complex **12** has the ligand in the partially delocalized form **8**. While molyb-

H^a H^b

Mo(CO)$_3$

10

H^a H^b

W(CO)$_3$

11

H^a H^b
H
H

Fe(CO)$_3$

12

denum and tungsten prefer coordination to a 6 π-system, which would be provided by either of the delocalized cations **7** or **9**, the iron atom prefers to coordinate with a 4 π-system, which is provided by the cation **8**.

The nmr spectrum of **12** has the signals for H-1, H-7 at τ 7.48, the ring protons are at higher field than those of **7**, and H^a, H^b both resonate near τ 8.5. The spectra of **10** and **11**, by contrast, show a large chemical shift difference between H^a and H^b; and the chemical shifts of the ring protons and H-1, H-7 are intermediate between those of **7** and **12**.

When substituted cyclooctatetraenes are protonated, then the homotropylium ions formed arise from protonation on the position next to the substituent. Thus methyl (**13a**) and phenylcyclooctatetraene (**13b**) give the corresponding 1-methyl (**14a**) and 1-phenylhomotropylium (**14b**) cations.

13a R = CH₃	**14a** R = CH₃
13b R = C₆H₅	**14b** R = C₆H₅

Chlorination of cyclooctatetraene has been shown to occur through the intermediate *endo*-chlorohomotropylium cation (**15**), which then reacts further to give *cis*-7,8-dichlorobicyclo[4.2.0]octa-2,4-diene (**16**) (see chapter 2).

In general it therefore appears that cyclooctatetraene is more readily attacked by electrophiles from a position inside the ring, and that the resulting cation is rearranged to the corresponding delocalized, 6 π-electron homotropylium cation. Protonation appears to occur preferentially at the position next to a substituent, but in all cases the homotropylium structure is thermodynamically more stable than the corresponding cyclooctatrienyl cation.

By analogy with the relationship between the tropylium ion and tropone, delocalization might be expected in 2,3-homotropone (**18**). This molecule was prepared by Holmes and Pettit by the sequence of reactions shown in Fig. 9.3. Addition of sodium hydroxide to the salt **12** gave the alcohol **17**, which on oxidation with chromium trioxide followed by removal of the iron tricarbonyl unit with ceric ammonium nitrate gave homotropone (**18**). The nmr spectrum suggests that there is little delocalization in this system, although an enhanced basicity of the carbonyl group was observed. Treatment of **18** with concentrated sulphuric acid or with HSbCl₆ gave the corresponding 2-hydroxyhomotropylium cation (**19**), obtained by the second method as the

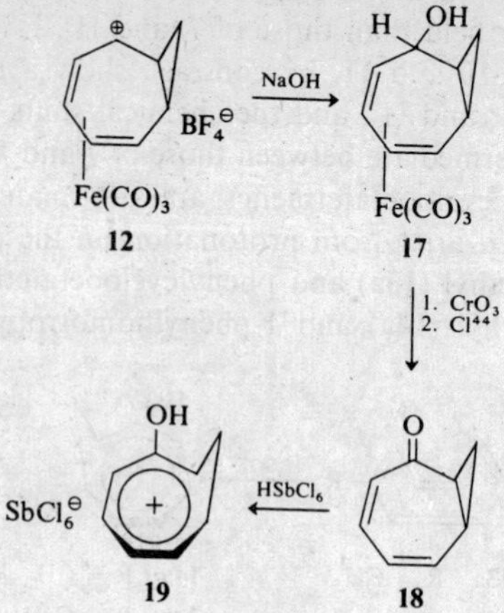

Figure 9.3

yellow, crystalline hexachloroantimonate. The nmr spectrum of 19 showed a downfield shift of the ring protons and three of the cyclopropyl protons, and an *upfield* shift of the remaining cyclopropyl hydrogen. The spectrum of 19 is thus consistent with this molecule having an open, delocalized structure. 4,5-Homotropone (20) has also been prepared, and this again appears to exhibit little delocalization through the cyclopropyl ring. Protonation of 20 gives the 4-hydroxyhomotropylium cation (21), which has the characteristic nmr spectrum of a homotropylium cation, the methylene cyclopropane hydrogens showing a chemical shift difference of τ 4·6. The corresponding 1-hydroxytropylium cation (22) has also been prepared, and

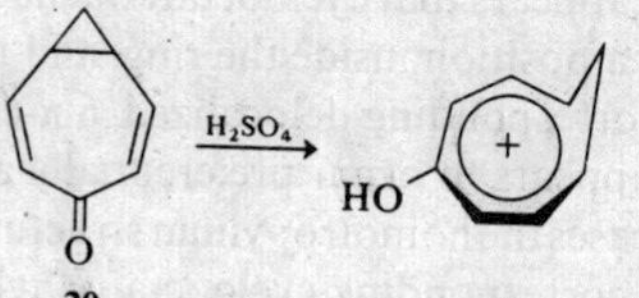

this again appears to be a delocalized homoaromatic species, which is stable at low temperatures but which is irreversibly rearranged to protonated acetophenone (23) at room temperature.

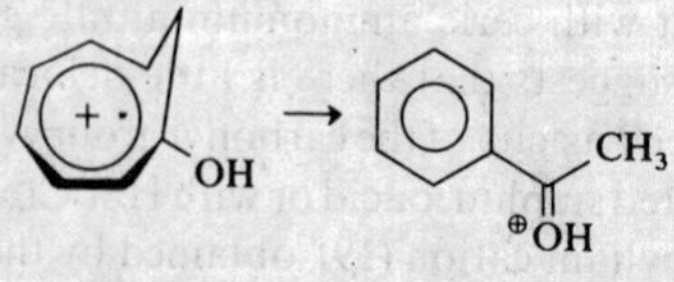

164

The homotropylium ions which have been described above all have the cyclic delocalized system interrupted by one methylene group. Recently a number of bishomotropylium cations have been prepared, in which the delocalized system is interrupted by two methylene groups. One example is the bicyclo-[4.3.1]decatrienium cation (**25**) which was prepared from the hydrocarbon **24** by protonation with fluorosulphonic acid in a mixture of sulphur dioxide and deuteromethylene chloride at $-75°$. The nmr spectrum of **25** shows

the H^3, H^4 protons at τ 1·99, the bridgehead protons H^1, H^6 at τ 5·56, and the remaining ring protons at ca τ 3·2. The proton H^b appears as a multiplet at τ 8·99, and the proton H^a as a doublet at τ 10·03. The rearrangement of **24** to the cation **25** indicates the enhanced stability of this ion, and the nmr spectrum is fully in accord with a delocalized structure.

A second bishomotropylium cation, the bicyclo[4.3.0]nonatrienium cation (**28**), has been prepared from the alcohol **26** by treatment with a mixture of fluorosulphonic acid and SO_2ClF at low temperature. The initial product is the cation **27**, which rearranges above $-125°$ to give **28**. The cation **28** can also be obtained by the similar treatment of the alcohol **29**. The nmr spectrum of **28** shows resonance signals at τ 1·77 (H^7, H^9), τ 2·48 (H^3, H^4), τ 2·62 (H^8), τ 3·60 (H^2, H^5), and τ 6·37 (H^1, H^6), and the spectrum supports a delocalized structure for this cation. The 1-methyl derivative of **28** has been prepared, and this system also appears to have a delocalized structure.

The properties of the homotropylium cations serve to indicate that there might be a second family of homoaromatic ions which are isoelectronic with the monocyclic ions discussed in chapter 4. Thus the corresponding homocyclopentadienyl anion (**30**) might be envisaged as the counterpart to the cyclopentadienyl anion. This anion has not so far been prepared, and in this case it may be less stable than the cyclohexadienyl anion (**31**), which can maintain a planar geometry without much bond angle distortion, unlike the cation **9**. However a bridged bishomocyclopentadienyl anion (**33**) has

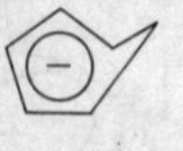

30

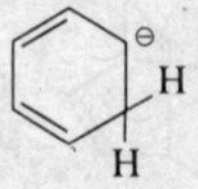

31

been prepared, analogous to **25**, in which delocalization appears to make an important contribution to the structure. Brown and Occolowitz first postulated **33** as being involved in the deprotonation of diene **32** which occurs $10^{4 \cdot 5}$ times faster than deprotonation of the corresponding monoene **34** (Fig. 9.4). The anion **33** was subsequently prepared by Brown by treatment

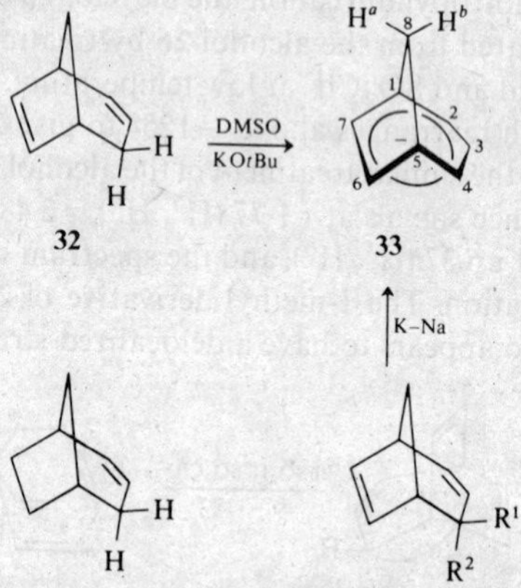

32 **33** **34**

35a $R^1 = OCH_3$, $R^2 = H$

35b $R^1 = H$, $R^2 = OCH_3$

Figure 9.4

of the methyl ether **35** with sodium-potassium alloy, and a similar preparation was also carried out by Winstein and his collaborators. Brown found that the *exo*-isomer, **35a**, reacted rapidly with the alloy in THF, whereas the *endo*-isomer, **35b**, reacted much more slowly. It appears likely that in the case of **35b** the proton is abstracted rather than the ether being cleaved. When solutions of **33**, prepared from **35a**, are quenched with a proton donor, such as water or methanol, then the hydrocarbon **32** is isolated. The nmr spectrum of **33** in THF-d$_8$ shows signals at $\tau 4\cdot59$ (H^3), $\tau 6\cdot35$ (H^6, H^7), $\tau 7\cdot13$ (H^2, H^4), $\tau 7\cdot45$ (H^1, H^5), $\tau 9\cdot13$ (H^a) and $\tau 9\cdot58$ (H^b). The symmetry of the spectrum supports the formation of at least a partially delocalized structure, and the *upfield* chemical shift of the H^6, H^7 protons and the *downfield* shift of the H^3 proton in **33** compared to the positions of these protons in **32** is indicative of the delocalization of the negative charge over the C-6, C-7 atoms. All of the proton chemical shifts are at high field for an aromatic system, and indicate that the diamagnetic ring current in **33** must be small. This view is supported by the finding of Bergman and Rajadhyaksha that the 2-bromobishomocyclopentadienyl anion **37** is not obtained by treatment of the bromide **36** with base, the product of the reaction being **38**. These workers suggest that **37** is formed, but that this subsequently loses Br$^\ominus$ and rearranges to **38**.

Examples of analogues of both the 6 π-electron species, the cyclopentadienyl anion and the tropylium cation have thus been prepared in which delocalization is interrupted by one or more methylene groups but which nevertheless appear to be delocalized, aromatic systems. The enhanced stability of the homotropylium cation appears to be greater than that of the bishomocyclopentadienyl anion, and it may be anticipated that an increase in the number of interrupting groups will decrease the importance of homoaromatic delocalization. The geometry of the system will also be expected to be important. In the 6 π-electron species it appears clear that, although some interaction may occur across a methylene group in the neutral species, such as cycloheptatriene, such effects are much more dramatically revealed in the case of ions. It is in the ionic species that other examples of homoaromatic systems containing 2 or 10 π-electrons might be expected, and these have indeed been found.

Katz and his co-workers found that treatment of 1,2,3,4-tetramethyl-3,4-dichlorocyclobutene (**39**) with silver hexafluoroantimonate at $-70°$ in sulphur dioxide gave the cation **40**. The cation **40** could also be prepared as the chloroaluminate by treatment of **39** with $AlCl_3$ in methylene chloride. The nmr spectrum of **40** showed that there were three types of methyl resonance, and in the ultraviolet spectrum the absorption maxima was found to occur at 253 nm, a position intermediate between that of the cyclopropenium cation (*ca* 185 nm) and the allyl cation (300 nm). The position of the ultraviolet maximum suggests that a large 1,3-interaction occurs in **40**, and a HMO calculation required a value of $\beta_{1,3} = 0.33\beta$, to account for the band position. A number of related cations were also examined, and all have similar nmr and ultraviolet spectra. The cation **40** thus appears to be an example of a homocyclopropenium cation.

In the 10 π-electron series it has been found that treatment of bicyclo-[6.1.0]nonatriene (**41**) in THF with a potassium mirror at $-80°$ gives the monohomocyclooctatetraenyl dianion **42** as the potassium salt. The nmr spectrum of the dianion **42** in DME-d_{10} shows a six-proton multiplet at

41   **42**

ca τ 4·8, due to the ring protons H^2 to H^7, a two-proton signal at τ 6·1 due to H^1, H^8 and signals at τ 8·0 and τ 10·0 due to H^b and H^a respectively. The small upfield shift of the ring protons (*ca* τ 0·7) and the *downfield* shift of the H^1, H^8 cyclopropyl protons (*ca* τ 2·8) compared to the position of these protons in **41**, clearly indicates that the charge is delocalized over the ring, and that the deshielding effect of the two added electrons is compensated by the presence of a diamagnetic ring current. This is further supported by the difference in chemical shift of the H^a, H^b protons. The dianion **42** is thus related to the cyclooctatetraenyl dianion, and, like the reduction of cyclo-octatetraene, the reduction of **41** can be arrested after the addition of only one electron. The monohomocyclooctatetraenyl radical anion (**43**) can be prepared either by treatment of **41** with potassium in DME or by electrolysis in liquid ammonia saturated with tetramethylammonium iodide. The anion radical **43** has a complex esr spectrum, but the hyperfine couplings have been determined. The protons on C-9 are non-equivalent and show a large differ-ence in the value of the splitting constants. The spectrum is best interpreted in favour of the delocalized structure **43**.

43

The 10 π-electron bridged monohomoaromatic cyclononatetraenyl anion **45** has been prepared by treatment of 1,6-methano[10]annulene (**44**) with the sodium methylsulphinyl carbanion in dimethylsulphoxide. The nmr spectrum of **45** supports the delocalized symmetrical structure.

$$CH_3SOCH_2$$

44   **45**

There is thus a range of ions containing 2, 6, and 10 π-electrons in which the cyclic delocalization is interrupted by one or more methylene groups, but which appear to be best represented as delocalized homoaromatic ions. These ions appear to be more stable than isomeric ions which are less delocalized and thus appears to be aromatic in the classical sense.

A second group of potentially aromatic systems has recently been postulated by Goldstein, who considered the possibility of aromatic conjugation in non-planar systems. Such a consideration arises out of the homoaromatic concept, since the overlap of the orbitals across the interfering atom is not a simple π-interaction. A simple m.o. treatment indicates that bicycloaromaticity will only occur in odd-systems in which the total number of π-electrons is 4n. Using this theory the ion **46** would be predicted to be bicycloaromatic, whereas **47** is bicycloantiaromatic. The theory further predicts that the stabilization of **46** will be *greater* than that of **48**, the second double bond

46   **47**   **48**

contributing to an increase in stability. These concepts are intuitively satisfying, in that the ion **46** may be considered to be resonating between the structures **46a** and **46b**, in which 6 π-electron bishomoaromatic systems are

46a   **46b**

present. However, this does give rise to certain difficulties in that a *tautomeric* rather than a mesomeric interaction between **46a** and **46b** might also lead

169

to the same effect. Hopefully, such a difference could be resolved by investigating the temperature dependence of the nmr spectrum, when, in the case of a tautomeric equilibrium between **46a** and **46b** the spectra due to the individual structures should become apparent.

At present the anion **46** and the corresponding 3-methyl derivative **50** are the only known examples of potentially bicycloaromatic ions. The anion **46**, which may be represented in the bicycloaromatic form as **46c**, shows in

46c

the nmr spectrum only four types of protons at τ 4·76 (H^3), τ 5·02 (H^6, H^7, H^8, H^9), τ 6·95 (H^2, H^4), and τ 7·71 (H^1, H^5). The spectrum and chemical shift positions are similar to those found in the bishomocyclopentadienyl anion (**33**). The 3-methyl anion **50** has only been implicated as an intermediate in the base catalysed deuterium exchange of the hydrocarbon **49**. In this case the corresponding system with only one double bond **51** has also been prepared, and this has been shown to exchange deuterium 750 times slower than **49**. This presumably indicates that the anion **50** is more stable than **52**.

However, in the case of both **50** and **46** bridge flipping tautomerism has not been excluded (although a maximum barrier height to flipping of 12 kcal. mole^{-1} has been put on **46**) and the enhanced stability may arise from this cause rather than from ' bicycloaromaticity '. Many more examples will be required to establish whether bicycloaromaticity is in fact a valid concept.

A third type of non-planar conjugative interaction has also been suggested in which the two interacting systems are joined through a single carbon atom. This has been termed spiroconjugation, and may be exemplified by

170

the structures **53** and **54**. Calculations for both types of systems have been made, predictions regarding the effects put forward, and some evidence for the occurrence of interactions of this type has been advanced. More activity in this area can be expected.

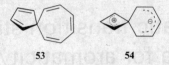

53 **54**

Further reading

For reviews on homoaromaticity see S. Winstein, *Chem. Soc. Special Publication* No 21, **5** (1967); *Quart. Revs.*, 1969, **23**, 141. For more recent references on homoaromaticity and bicycloaromaticity see S. W. Staley and D. W. Reichard, *J. Am. Chem. Soc.*, 1969, **91**, 3998; and references therein; P. Ahlberg, D. L. Harris, and S. Winstein, *J. Am. Chem. Soc.*, 1970, **92**, 4454 and references therein.

For the original reference on bicycloaromaticity see M. J. Goldstein, *J. Am. Chem. Soc.*, 1967, **89**, 6357; and for those on spiroconjugation see H. E. Simmons and T. Fukunaga, *J. Am. Chem. Soc.*, 1967, **89**, 5208; and R. Hoffmann, A. Imamara, and G. D. Zeiss, *J. Am. Chem. Soc.*, 1967, **89**, 5215.

10. Aromatic transition states and criteria for aromaticity

10.1 Aromatic transition states

As may be seen from the discussion in the foregoing chapters, the concept of aromaticity pervades many areas of organic chemistry. The delocalization of π-electrons over a number of atoms in a cycle has been shown to lower the energy, *providing* that there are sufficient bonding molecular orbitals to accommodate the electrons in a closed shell. As we have seen, the advantages of delocalization are emphasized in charged systems, since delocalization has the added effect of spreading the charge over a number of atoms. It might therefore be expected that a similar delocalization of π-electrons occurring in the transition state of a reaction should lower the energy of that state and allow the reaction to proceed more easily. This concept of aromatic stabilization has recently been shown to be extremely useful theoretically, and may be applied to a variety of reactions. As Dewar has pointed out, the first suggestion of such a stabilization was put forward by Evans to account for the facility with which the Diels–Alder reaction occurs. This reaction in its simplest form can be exemplified by the reaction of butadiene (1) with ethylene (2) to give cyclohexene (3). The transition state of

this reaction may be envisaged to occur through the interaction of the 4 $2p$ π-atomic orbitals on the diene 1 with the 2 $2p$ π-orbitals on the dienophile 2, as shown in Fig. 10.1 (i). The set of 6 atomic orbitals can then form 6 molecular orbitals, three of which are bonding and which can accommodate the 6 π-electrons. The problem can be seen to be very similar to that of benzene discussed in chapter 1, except that the interaction between the terminal atoms of the two reactants resembles a homoaromatic rather than a pure π-interaction. The interaction of butadiene (1) with itself can now be seen to have a transition state made up of the 8 $2p$ π-atomic orbitals, as shown in Fig. 10.1 (ii), and this transition state resembles the orbital arrangement of

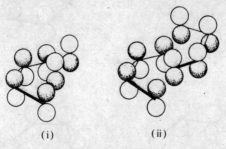

(i) (ii)

Figure 10.1 (i) p_π Atomic orbitals, involved in a 4 + 2 cycloaddition, (ii) p_π atomic orbitals involved in a 4 + 4 cycloaddition.

planar cyclooctatetraene. There are only three bonding orbitals for 8 π-electrons, and 2 electrons will have to enter a non-bonding orbital. This is an unfavoured state and, as is well known, this type of addition does not readily occur. *Suprafacial* addition, to use the terminology of Woodward and Hoffmann, will only take place in a concerted fashion when the transition state contains $4n + 2$ π-electrons. The concept of the aromatic transition state gives, of necessity, the same prediction as that enunciated by the Woodward–Hoffmann rules.

These types of arguments can be applied to other types of reactions besides cycloadditions. The transition state for the conversion of hexatriene (**4**) into cyclohexadiene (**5**) can be assumed to involve the 6 $2p_\pi$ orbitals, as

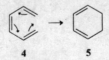

4 **5**

shown in Fig. 10.2. The ring closure may occur in two ways, either by rotation of the 1,6 atoms in the opposite direction (10.2 (i)) or in the same direction (10.2 (ii)). Rotation of the atoms in opposite directions was termed *disrotatory* by Woodward and Hoffmann, and in the same direction, *conrotatory*. As will be seen from the figure, disrotation leads to a combination of the 6 orbitals which resembles benzene, whereas conrotation leads to a set of orbitals with a sign inversion. Disrotation should be the stereochemical course of this electrocyclic reaction, a prediction again in harmony with the Woodward–Hoffmann rules. The arrangement of atomic orbitals attained by conrotatory ring closure in hexatriene is the configuration found in a Möbius strip, and Heilbronner had predicted that such an arrangement might be the preferred

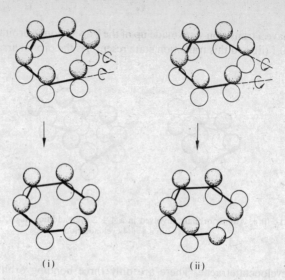

Figure 10.2 (i) Disrotatory ring closure in hexatriene, (ii) conrotatory ring closure in hexatriene.

orbital configuration in $4n$ annulenes. Zimmerman extended this idea to electrocyclic reactions. The two states for butadiene are shown in Fig. 10.3. In this $4n$-system it is the conrotatory mode (10.3 (ii)) that gives the Möbius configuration, and this has been shown experimentally to be the actual stereospecific mode of ring closure. The ground state ring closure of $4n + 2$

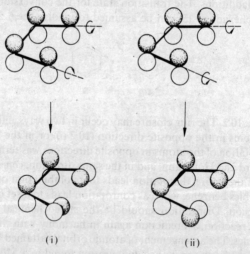

Figure 10.3 (i) Disrotatory ring closure in butadiene, (ii) conrotatory ring closure in butadiene.

π-electron systems is thus predicted to occur by disrotatory ring closures via Hückel transition states, whereas the $4n$ π-electron ground state ring closures should occur by conrotation via Möbius transition states. In the first excited state it is readily seen that these rules are reversed, the $4n + 2$ system closing via Möbius transition states and the $4n$ by Hückel transition states.

An advantage of this method over other approaches to orbital symmetry correlations is that only the number of interacting atomic orbitals need be known for the prediction of the probable stereochemistry and pathway of lowest energy for these type of reactions. The atomic orbitals may be either of the p_π or p_σ type, and the retro-Diels–Alder and the retro-ring closures are thus also predicted to occur, in the latter case with the correct stereochemistry.

It will have been noted that the arrangement of atomic orbitals in Figs. 10.1 to 10.3 closely resembles the arrangement of orbitals of a homoaromatic interaction (Fig. 9.1). Consequently, it is not surprising that homoaromatic transition states should have been invoked in a number of reactions involving charged species. Thus acetolysis of cis-bicyclo[3.1.0]hex-3-yl toluenesulphonate (6) gives the corresponding cis-acetate 8 as sole product with complete retention of configuration. The acetolysis proceeds faster than that of the corresponding trans-epimer and the increased rate and stereospecificity of the product is attributed to the intervention of the trishomocyclopropenium cation 7. Deuteration studies supported the formation of a

symmetrical transition state. Similarly, a bishomocyclopropenium cation 10 has been invoked to describe the transition state for the solvolysis of anti-7-norbornenyl toluenesulphonate (9). In this case the cation 10 has been generated with SbF_5-FSO_3H at $-50°$, and the nmr spectrum at low

temperature is reasonably consistent with the assigned structure. The proton at C-7 is at considerably higher field (τ 6·7) than the protons at C-2, C-3 (τ 2·93) which tends to indicate that the homoaromatic character of this system is small.

Thus as would be expected, aromatic delocalization appears to be favoured as a means of lowering the energy of transition states, and it is perhaps not surprising that the attainment of such a delocalized state has a profound effect on the course of chemical reactions and the nature of the products.

10.2   Criteria for aromaticity

Throughout the preceding chapters an attempt has been made to distinguish between 'aromatic' and 'non-aromatic' systems. Such a choice requires that some criteria are being used in order that this selection can be carried out, and in section 2.6 some of the problems in establishing these criteria were examined. In this final section the various criteria of aromaticity will again be examined in the light of the properties of the various compounds that have been described.

The classical criteria of stability and lack of reactivity can be discounted, since both of these properties depend on the difference in energy between the ground state and excited states of the system, and not on the ground state energy of the system itself. Similar objections apply to the electronic spectrum. Although all of these phenomena are useful in comparing molecules which are closely related in structure, such as the benzenoid polycyclic hydrocarbons, they are not suitable as criteria for distinguishing the presence or absence of aromaticity.

As was suggested in section 2.6, the properties which are principally dependent upon the ground state of the system and which are most readily observed are those involving the magnetic behaviour of the molecule. In aromatic systems the enhanced diamagnetic susceptibility appears to be the most generally observed property, and it can be observed in three ways: (i) by measurement of the anisotropy of a single crystal, (ii) by the determination of the diamagnetic susceptibility exaltation, and (iii) by its effect upon the nmr spectrum. Each measurement has both advantages and disadvantages as compared with the others. The diamagnetic anisotropy measurement demands the formation of a single crystal, and the correlation of the magnetic axes of the crystal with the axes of the constituent molecules. However, the measurement of the anisotropy, due to the circulation of electrons over the cycle, does appear to be the most fundamental observation of aromaticity of the three types of measurement. The diamagnetic susceptibility exaltation (Λ) is more readily measured and does not require the formation of a crystal nor, consequently, a knowledge of the orientation of the molecules. However, it does require fairly large samples and, more importantly, it depends on knowing the calculated diamagnetic anisotropy of a theoretical, but *unreal*, molecule. The nmr spectrum is the easiest to observe, as the many examples discussed in preceding chapters will have shown, requires only a few milligrams of sample and the orientation of the sample is unimportant. However, the actual chemical shifts of the protons in the nmr spectrum are not simply dependent on any one factor, and even the chemical shift positions in aromatic compounds are widely varied.

Attempts to relate these phenomena to the degree of aromaticity, that is, use these criteria quantitatively, are fraught with difficulty. The use of nmr chemical shifts for such a purpose can be completely discounted, and both values such as Λ per unit area from the diamagnetic exaltation or $K_3/[(K_1 + K_2)/2]$ from the diamagnetic anisotropy are likely to be only crude quantitative indicators of the degree of aromaticity.

Although there have been objections to the general concept of ring current to explain the magnetic properties of cyclic delocalized systems, nevertheless it is now generally accepted that a conjugated cyclic system will show either a diamagnetic or paramagnetic shielding effect depending on the number of π-electrons in the system. Systems can be classified into three types depending on the type of shielding observed. *Paratropic* systems will show paramagnetic ring current shielding in the nmr spectrum, *diatropic* systems will show diamagnetic ring current shielding, and *atropic* systems will show no shielding effect arising from ring current effects. It will usually be the case that paratropic systems will be antiaromatic, diatropic systems aromatic, and atropic systems nonaromatic, but this does not necessarily follow. Such a classification removes the problem of describing a system in terms of its ' aromaticity ' and thus invoking the multitude of properties that surround this concept, but it does not remove the problem of aromaticity itself.

A second ground state property which might appear preferable to the magnetic property as a criterion is the C—C bond lengths of aromatic systems. Such a criterion would appear to be excellent for the annulenes. In non-aromatic or antiaromatic systems an alternation of the bond lengths is to be expected, whereas in the aromatic annulenes all the bond lengths should be the same, and approach the 1·39 Å length of the benzene C—C bond. This criterion seems to be largely met in the annulenes, although it may be observed that even in [18]annulene the C—C bonds are not all equal, although they do not alternate. However, when this property of bond length is applied to heterocyclic or polycyclic systems, wide variations of bond length are likely. Although such differences could be overcome by using other model compounds (e.g., the C—N and C—C bond lengths in pyridine), the technique is still fairly lengthy and difficult to apply, and suitable crystals also require preparation.

The criteria for aromaticity which we have discussed above have all been concerned with experimentally observable properties. A second approach may be envisaged in which aromatic compounds could be defined in terms of some theoretical property, such as ' that all the π-electrons must complete a closed shell of bonding orbitals '. However, as should now be obvious to the reader, such a definition depends on the present state of the art of the theorist, and is not very satisfying to the experimental chemist. The definition advanced for aromatic compounds in section 2.6 still appears to be the best, and can now be stated more succinctly.

Aromatic compounds are diatropic cyclic molecules in which all the ring atoms are involved in a single conjugated system.

Further reading

For the authors' own account of the Woodward–Hoffmann Rules, see R. B. Woodward and R. Hoffmann, *The Conservation of Orbital Symmetry*, Verlag Chemie, 1970.

For Dewar's views on this subject see *The Molecular Orbital Theory of Organic Chemistry*, McGraw-Hill, 1969, and *Tetrahedron*, Suppl. 8, 1966, 75.

For the Möbius strip as a chemical concept, see E. Heilbronner, *Tetrahedron Letters*, 1964, 1923; H. E. Zimmerman, *J. Am. Chem. Soc.*, 1966, **88**, 1564, 1566.

For other examples of homoaromatic transition states see S. Winstein, *Chem. Soc. Special Publication*, No. 21, 1967, p. 5; R. E. Leone and P. von R. Schleyer, *Angew. Chem. Int. Ed. Eng.*, 1970, **9**, 860.

For a further discussion of aromatic character see A. J. Jones, *Rev. Pure and Applied Chemistry*, 1968, **18**, 253.

Index